BLUEBERRY
DREAMS

BLUEBERRY DREAMS

Stimulate the Inner You

Calvin Earl Dallas

1603 Capitol Ave., Suite 310 Cheyenne, Wyoming USA 82001
1-888-980-6523 | admin@urlinkpublishing.com

URLink Print and Media is committed to excellence in the publishing industry.

Book design copyright © 2021 by URLink Print and Media. All rights reserved.

Published in the United States of America

Library of Congress Control Number: 2021923590
ISBN 978-1-68486-033-3 (Paperback)
ISBN 978-1-68486-034-0 (Hardback)
ISBN 978-1-68486-035-7 (Digital)

05.11.21

I WAS IN AN UNDERGROUND building led by a beautiful woman who showed me a beautiful plant that I held, but it died, then she said she would assist me to bring it back to life. She left me, and I knocked on the door of another lady, who showed me another place. Last night, I dreamt I was in a place or countryside similar to an ocean shoreline or a beach. I met two beings of dark complexion, male and female. These beings were very different from humans. On earth, their heads were a little bit bigger, and their spirits seemed not to be of humans. These beings prayed to the Lord and prayed with me. I felt that they were my spiritual parents from another realm or dimension.

Also, I found myself in a faraway country setting; it was very rural, with mountains, trees, grass, and water. I met a person there. He said to me,

"Welcome to this realm or dimension of a far-out country."

I was very shocked because I knew I was fully conscious on another realm, but I didn't want to journey out, so I just prayed the Lord's Prayer.

Someone put or glued my book to the ceiling. I tried to retrieve it with the help of a friend. But the material we used was too heavy. I was in some type of school, so I wanted to report it to principal. I wanted to get paid. There were many women in the dream.

One brother had caught an ugly short snake. I ran when he put it down.

I saw a new Saint Thomas; it had always been there, but I never saw it.

I was retrained in work, almost like a slave but still looked upon with respect and reverence.

I was talking on the telephone to a blond black woman; she was better.

I was caught in an underground room with a friend, knowing I would wake up eventually, out of the room into another realm.

The room spun around as I talked to the dream merchant.

I destroyed a snake, but another snake appeared, which was enormous. It was in a swamp or lake, and only the head was visible. This snake was going swallow a whole man, but a giant chain pulled the man out of the snake's mouth.

She had a salty kiss. I am sure it was her. She seemed real.

Dad made dinner.

I picked up a pretty little lady; she looked funny on my arm. In a place that was similar to Milwaukee, a group of people and my brother were socializing. There were many sweets in my mother's house: cakes, donuts, cereals, everything for the taking. In an office, a certain woman kept touching me with her shoe and other people were going to take a test. As I walked down the street, it got cooler. I wore a nice orange suit with a turban.

I was completely naked in a mansion that was elaborate to the hilt. It had rooms that you could go through from door to door. The rooms were splendid, out of sight, and at the same time, there was a man who came to visit, and he was talking to her about some deal. All the time, I hid in nature, observing her with him. He was kind of light skinned, around his early forties or late thirties. He played saxophone, and at one point in the conversation, he started to swing in a jazz lyric, with his voice in it. He sounded good, as if he was making love; for an old-timer, he was pretty good. I saw myself in nature at first, watching him and her through the trees. The trees seemed to hide me. Her daughter came out with a long thin white smoke. I told her to get back to her mother who was coming. She didn't respond; she just puffed on the white jay. Then her mother entered the picture and didn't get mad but told her something and followed her back in the house. Apparently, they didn't see me. She was followed through the house in each room by the man, as he was talking to her. I was naked, slipping from one room to another, because each room had a door to it that led to the next. The house was magnificent.

She told the man that she was glad that he could come, and she hoped to see the deal work. The man asked her what she was going to do with the boy who sold T-shirts. He did well in the community. It seemed that it was very peaceful in nature. Something told me to go in nature where there were a lot of trees to listen to. The quiet would be extremely helpful.

At one point, a big leaf came off a tree, as I observed from my hidden position in nature, and the man stopped talking and looked at it. He had come to see her or a woman similar to her, but he broke up our meeting, so I hid in the tree leaves because I didn't want him to see me, as I was nude.

When I saw her in the mansion, she had a beautiful garment on that went up to her neck. She was dressed elegantly. There were no jealous feelings from me toward the man, just that I should stay away from him and not let him see me. I wanted her to find me in a mansion like this one. Now I realize that in this mansion, I had the ability to observe something and not be seen by going through the various doors in the house, or dimensions, or hiding, or centering myself in nature, as becoming or being a part of it but, at the same time, being unique.

I helped a lady up the stairs; she said nobody had ever helped her before. I said I wanted to help you, then another woman jumped on my back. Finally, when I got her up the stairs, she gave me a big hug.

I had a flower growing out of it; some of the skin was puffed up. I pulled at the flower, and a white substance came out. I could feel it drain out of me.

Mother made a shirt for Essie; it was very short.

I was on top of the murderer. I controlled him. I came back into the dwelling, and the nurse or attendant offered me coffee in a strange way.

I did not put it in my mouth, and it was coming more to life. Blossoming, she introduced me to another woman who liked me very much.

I was dancing with a vessel that I was rubbing to create a soft sound rhythm; other people were there partying too.

I was late for teaching a class at a school. I went to apologize to the teacher. She was okay with it, but I was in a room with my neighbor. She gave me refreshments, sweets that didn't want, but she made me eat straight from her own hand, and then we sat down on the couch.

In my dream, I took a picture of some type of machine that seemed to be very different and futuristic, made of various metals, in gray color and dark values, and there seemed to be steam coming out of it. I took a middle shot and long shot of it; I noticed that the film hadn't been put into the camera.

I was with a lady who caressed me; her skin felt kind of rough, as she hugged me. I asked her if she had been burned; she said yes. We caressed a little.

I was with a beautiful lady; we had cookies together. I tried to get someone else to talk to her. She was beautiful. I have a lot of hair, and I combed it.

I saw a woman who was light skinned. She smiled at me while she looked closely at me. She was with a young man and some children, and she seemed to like me very much.

I was in the balcony and started to come down. I noticed that one man was watching me closely, so I changed my position and came down another way.

I was with the lovely lady intimately; I could really feel being with her.

The band was waiting patiently for me. They played several songs, but I never got to play my trumpet.

There were buckets of paints in the road; it seemed as though someone was trying to paint the road outside my house, but it looked non-artistic and noncreative. I tried to complain, but no one would listen. I found myself putting exact steel needles into a system that required that I move a parked white car outside the road. That's when the party started. There were different guests that came to her. Two men played the trumpet; they were good, and I went outside and saw that they had another celebration with and for a special group. Then I saw various ladies; some were thick and some were thin.

I was in a store and saw items or vitamins in various colored bottles in details.

I picked up a creative vessel and looked inside and outside.

I met a very powerful runner. He jumped over a car as he ran past me. He came back to meet me, and I told him my name. He told me his and shook my hand. "Run with chi," I explained to him the idea of internal power. I met his coach. I knew him, and I even put my hand on his shoulder and said, "You're a great coach."

They seemed to be talking in a different language; they got in a car to leave.

We were riding on the back of a large worm who could talk. We rode through a big city, and I asked it if it knew how to get to Twenty-Third Street. The worm, who had the personality of a brother, said yes.

I was at a party where I was having fun with two white women that I knew, but in another part of the party, they seemed to be unaware of me. I was with some other people.

It was a dark night. I was being followed by cars with bright lights, next to a large body of water, and finally, I got away from the cars and hid in a bushy green area of plants. I saw a huge crocodile coming swiftly across the water. When it arose vertically out of the water, I could see it had a human face.

The elevator brought me back to a level where I could go out into the city, but at first, it took me very deep. I was with a beautiful white lady; we seemed to be in a family situation.

I was with some friends, going to a neighborhood that reminded me of my hometown. When I got there, my friend let me go upstairs to relax or to watch TV. He had a big house. His sisters and brothers brought me refreshments to eat.

I was in a music shop. I saw many different horns. I saw a very unique horn; the owner said it was digital and that I could try it. In a crowd of people, one person came up to me and put an instrument that was very thin to my neck, and then he said I could continue. I played with soul and heart. I went to look for my bag that I had put down on the outside of the music store window, but it was gone. The owner had given me some paper that seemed to be money, but the people who heard me play had given me money also. I didn't have enough money for the horn, which was fifty dollars. The music store owner said it was all right for me to send him the money in the mail. He knew that I had to catch a plane at five o'clock.

I was helping children practice for a marching drill; I met a man who I talked to about the technique of the drill, but I couldn't find my cell phone. There was a woman who watched me closely because I was looking in someone else's bag for my cell phone. I told her I was looking for my cell phone; she listened carefully.

My aunt was driving me to a store. I got out and bought some food, particularly some ice cream. When I went in the store, a man was watching me when I paid for my items. I told several men, "You don't think that I have the money?" I said, "I come here all the time and I paid. "They seemed to be happy when I talked to them in this way.

My mother told me to do a certain task. I didn't feel like doing it. She said I was a leader now.

My father was sleeping with the light on. I asked him if it was bothering him, and he said no. I brushed my teeth, then I was listening to my father tell me and my other brothers and sisters a family story. I felt he was a genius.

The light-skinned lady was talking to someone else, then she jumped into my lap. I could see her face closely and feel her soft butt. I kissed her a lot and then I entered her. I thought of impregnating her, and then I pulled out.

The three or two ladies, after we had played entertaining games, disappeared from the room.

The people, mostly women, kept coming closer to me. For me, it seemed as though they were after my blood, so I hit them on the head to stop them, but they seemed to keep coming, looking forward to the hit on the head.

I had an amazing dream of making love to a white woman, and then afterward, she said she got to go. Okay, just like that, oral sex. The whole ball of wax was great and soft.

I was in different bedrooms, but they all had bars on their windows, like jails.

I made love to a lizard-like or reptilian female creature, and I seemed to ejaculate some essence quickly into her body. I had difficulty putting my penis into her opening; only one-fourth went in because my penis was not totally hard. The reptilian she-being was determined to get to me, but I was trying to avoid her. Finally, I gave in, and that's when I just made love to her. She just let me do it from the backside.

I was with the brothers, getting ready to give a show of black talent and lecture form.

I was in survival mode and saw beautiful woman who wanted to help me, but I had to get out of my emotions and had no clothes on.

A driver drove us, a group of people, up a long hill that was ninety degrees; he always drove very fast.

Austin had a brand-new car, a station wagon. He said he wanted to talk, but I talked too fast and did not let him tell me what he wanted to talk about. I was just having fun. I was given a bundle of money by a guy in a car.

I was in a dream where I was attacked by a martial artist, and I neutralized him with soft gin; I put a great amount in his body.

A beautiful lady rescued me from some wannabe criminal who, when the time came to do me in, became shy and backed down. I noticed I had some unseen friends standing by just in case. As I stood there with this lady, she wanted a piece of cloth I had. When I was about to give it to her, I looked down and saw that we were so high up on some type of mountain or another dimension, inside out.

My friend Gilbert stood in front of me. His vibe was on me heavily, saying that he wanted to date a black woman. I had already told him that he would be successful in front of his girlfriend, but it would not be easy. He wanted to go to the club and wanted to know. "What about your girlfriend? "He said she doesn't know what she wants.

Gregg was in the car with me. I kept calling him Dallas. I bought some cookies for him. He got some cookies for me. He called me James the Second. I was called James Dallas II.

I saw Mom lying in bed, and she said she thinks Essie is fine.

I was at a party. I kept leaving and going back to the party until everyone was gone.

I was with a great lady.

I saw a big snake under the water; it looked dead, but on top of the ground, part of it was moving.

I was on a country road at night, and a man had a tied barking dog. I waited until the man said it was okay to proceed. As I proceeded, I saw several greyhound dogs in an underground place, just standing quietly. Than all of a sudden, one of the dogs took off running. I could see him run rapidly through several tunnels until he came to a dead end.

There were three women talking to me in a house, then they left. I noticed that I had been in this house before. One door was left open that led to energy that I did not want, so I closed that door. Then I saw a young boy hiding under a bed. The whole house was very quiet; it felt very creepy. All of a sudden, another young man came into the house and sat on the floor; he said that the devil got his mind messed up. I thought, *You are the only devil.* Then the young man looked at me. I recognized him, and he recognized me. He said, "Mr. Dallas." Then we both smiled.

There were thousands of insects flying around; I was trying to hang a unique piece of artwork. My mother was downstairs cooking.

I am in a series of neighborhoods, trying to get away from dogs.

Again, I am trying to get away from dogs with another person, but all of a sudden, I realize that I have locked myself in with a dog behind me, then here, a voice said, "Come, dog," but there is no dog; it is in my mind.

I am in a college, trying to register for the courses that I need. Someone is in front of me. I asked him to pass; at first, he said no then yes. I passed him, went to the door of the office, and saw that the people were taking a lunch break.

The women gave me some hard blows. They seemed to be angry.

I was in a beautiful city, running in the sky with other runners, and I heard a voice tell me to fly swiftly into a skyscraper room. So I did; the feeling was great.

Working with several women, everything was going smooth. I saw an old girlfriend come into the picture, but a man met me and one of my associate lady friends and caused her to leave me when he said Dallas was a businessman.

I carried my mother to look at a pool or water complex that we lived at. It was going to overflow. I wanted her to see how the water was coming up. She let me carry her. She could not walk. She felt secure and good in my arms. I wanted her to be safe, so I carried her to see the water. However, when we finally saw it, it was rumbling up but did not overflow yet.

She appeared very light skinned now; she held on to me tight the whole way. She had no weight and was very sleepy.

I went to a village, where I shopped in a bakery and a store. I could not find the things or items that I needed. I met some children in the village; one boy was named Calvin. He said he had heard of me. I introduced myself to him. I tried to find my way back to the village. Then I came back to my apartment, and it looked different. My sister, Barbara, was there. It was the same size, but all the walls were some type of dark glass. There were many people there who, all of a sudden, showed up there. There was a small cat on the floor, a young black cat. I picked it up, and it gave me a feeling of great warmth and love. I noticed that the cat turned into a young woman, who sat on the sofa beside me. I introduce myself to the other people as Calvin, and they responded slowly but finally told me their names. One person seemed to preach about God for a long time. I was standing and listening. One woman said I looked great in the suit that I had on. She said that I looked better than another man who had worn the suit. As I looked at the suit that I had on, it was black and had small white checks, but my shirt was not in my pants; it could have been a style.

Heavy equipment with people in it drill into the earth to fight each other with weapons; the heavy transport machines with people in them finally came up to the surface again. Some of the people were not hurt, but some were. A question was asked: "So this is how you destroy Patrick?"

"Yes, by pulling on the line."

The bathroom was flooding, so I got up from the water, but then a little girl came in my place and stole my money. I put clothes on and ran after her and got my money back.

There was a cook who made a vegetable egg omelet. He wanted me to try it; I did, then he made me a veggie burger. I wanted to give him forty dollars, the tip included.

Saw myself inside of a mountain, creating a home.

We ate a tasteless green cactus-looking plant, with long stems. I asked the people whom I was with, "Does this plant get you high?" and they said it would seem too spiritually. There were about five people in the group.

The lady made me lunch, but at first, she said she wanted fifteen, then she changed her mind and said twenty. I said only fifteen, as she had said in the beginning. She left and went somewhere. I fought and argued with her; she asked me to be quiet, so I did. I paid her fifteen and took the lunch.

In this dream, there was a beautiful light-skinned girl. I fell in love with her. I went to her house. I tried to mail a card in a city that I had never been in before, and somehow, I found myself at her house. I liked her, and she liked me. We started to kiss; we liked each other's lips. Her father was coming to the house; somehow, I came out of the house and met him. He was short and covered with a box costume. However, before he came, I noticed that the door in the house was shorter than her and me, so I told her so. Back to her father, I asked him why.

One person regretted a lovely dark sister; she was with another beautiful black sister. The next thing I knew, I was in a house in the dining room or kitchen, sitting at a table. My tai chi student was good. I was reaching down this long table, trying to get some water; my whole body was almost across the table. I noticed a very beautiful black lady at the table, but she was not sitting down. I asked her would she not like to sit down. She smiled and said yes. All the time I was with her, I sensed that this woman had a big stomach. So she sat down on my lap. I sniffed her fragrance from her silky cheek, and she put my hand on her stomach. I felt her protruding oval-shaped stomach; it felt solid as a rock, and at that moment, it all felt so real.

I visited my two younger brothers. I heard them play a musical song together in a room. The door was closed. I was on the outside, but I could still see inside. The harmony was good, but somewhere along the line, they were not holding the notes long enough. I advised them on this point. In addition, I told them to stay scientific and to not get emotional about what I had said. I informed them that I had played in many bands. They waited for me in a limousine, but I never got there on time, so they drove away.

The hideous monster poked itself constantly and was very fat and large. It ran after little people. It seemed that it would eat them. While in the bank, an army seized and locked up the people. They were all dressed in white because some substance was sprayed throughout the room or bank. The people looked controlled. It seemed that the hideous monsters waited for these people on the upper level. Then they would eat them.

I visited X, and she was very happy in her garden, dancing and singing. I wanted her to let me in to see her, but saying something about me, that had to do with magic. I was very cool when I heard her talking about me. However, in a matter of seconds, I was sitting next to her, very close.

I could feel her energy. She was totally in shock and frozen. I told her that I loved her several times, but she remained in shock. Therefore, I decided to leave, but I found that her energy did not allow me to leave.

You get married in May, and how about you?

I helped the young woman down the stairs.

The boat was very fast. The others and I rode in it down the street. They stopped to get beers.

Mrs. Venue was talking to Ms. Donor in a small house in a backyard about a child. I went in talking to Mrs. Divan. Mrs. Benzene was very quiet to the point of ignoring me, and since she doesn't want to acknowledge me, I went in the yard and wrote something down on the paper, then I left and went to one part of the city. Then I came back to see Mrs. Divan was still there with Mrs. Benzene. Several cars passed me, red, black, and another black. They pulled into the house next door. In the backyard, I was looking for a book that I left on the table; I saw it and picked it up. I heard someone in the garage or the little house in the backyard, running water. I asked out loud, "Is that you, Mrs. Divan?" Then she said, "Don't forget the children's clothes." I told her I am not going to touch them.

They seemed to be a happy couple; they lived in a great house. One day, they argued; next thing you know, they separated. She was doing something different; he bought a new motorcycle part. He was supposed to go to a special meeting, but he fell asleep; some person whom he knew and a man came by his house and woke him up. The operator talked to him about himself and some of the things he did. He washed his dishes for him. The other man got up and started to move around. There was a dog in the house that should not be in the house or around. He threatened the dog by telling the dog that he will get his gun if the dogs didn't leave. The dog left immediately. The man realized that he had missed his class. So he thought about going to the university with his friends.

We were on the train. One person got sick, a man, I told him to let his vomit out the window. My brother, the oldest one, was with a woman. Two other men sat behind them. They tried to attack him. I kept them away and told them that they had to learn to control themselves. I had been there and had to control myself. When the bus stopped, the bus driver asked a person who was almost not conscious as to where they would set up their business; he did not know if the person in charge of this had put everything in order. I got off the bus to check if the driver was still there, and he was. In the station, someone was eating a sandwich.

I was in my college room, early for my class, so I decided to play my trumpet, but I forgot it. A man on a bus-type vehicle took it off a shelf in front of him. He gave it to me and said some encouraging words. When I took it from him and left the bus, everyone on the bus was happy and said goodbye. I went back to the classroom and saw that it was full of people. I noticed a young woman in the room; I wanted to sit by her. There was another chair, empty, by a man who seemed to be smoking. I wanted to go in the room through the back door, but I noticed there was none. So I went through the front door. I came to the girl who had been playing the trumpet, she seemed to be in an upstairs level in the room, but as I got close to her, she began to look like a seal. I tried not to look at her directly, but I could sense that she was aware of me noticing her change because she did not try to attract me, even though she was focused on me.

She was beautiful, light skinned, smiling. I nodded several times to her child. It seemed as though I knew the cute little light-skinned girl, and she nodded back in the same manner.

Her mother came close to me, touched my eye gently, and said, "You hurt your eye."

She laughed and said it was a test, then she gave me a tender wet kiss and laughed.

The person gave me four hundred, but I only deposited three hundred. Happy, I went to the other world of the best. In a small room, I waited for the best.

Riding on a bus with Charles, I found a purse with a device in it. A girl's purse. Charles was very skinny; he was even lighter than his shirt. The bus driver detached me. I was in a different country, maybe Russia. They would lead me across the border with the device; they wanted me to pay thirty thousand. However, I just signed my name. Two women in a strange house where I was shooting images on a mirror or glass photo screen with light. They said I had taken their internet device. We were captured by the officials again. There was a friend of mine who saw us, and he was shooting at the officials to help us get away.

My brother Leslie had brought beer for a beer party. I wondered why he had gone to town. He left after stocking the cooler with beer. I felt that someone would try to take the beer. We had a fight with some people, one was very large. He was knocked out; we were in a jail which was like a home. This is where they punish you for not doing what they say. I escaped and went to a temporary home. When I left that home, I was free; a little girl came after me as I was walking down the street. She returned to her play. I saw my brother enter into a new house down the road. I went into the house, and he had his back turned to me. I hit him with a rolled-up newspaper. He turned around, and I asked him how it felt; it was Denzel Washington. He was not surprised; he made a factual statement with no emotion. I left the place crying. He followed to see where I was going. I fell down crying.

Carla was talking to my mother, and my mother told me that she said I had to leave my house. I went to her and tried to tell her off, but she was very bigheaded with superior confidence.

I had just finished taking a shower. So I went downstairs. Mom was preparing all types of green leafy vegetables to eat. I moved out of her way several times, as I watched her rinse the vegetables with water. I told her I hadn't eaten anything yet; she suggested that I go downstairs in the basement where there was food to eat.

I met Carla in my house. I told her that she was a man and a woman but sometimes too tough; she embraced me with a loving and caring mood. I touched her arm and felt that she still loved me very much. She was very full-figured in the dream and healthy. I saw her helping other young black men.

People were calling my name from a huge ocean liner; I wanted to escape from the attention, so I changed my route of walking to a back alleyway. I saw a crow-like bird in my way jump up and fly. A black dog, with pointy ears and a slim body, came after me. I ran up the stairs of a building close by and tried to open the door but could not. As I looked back to see what the dog was doing, it was just looking at me calmly, then I woke up.

In a dream, a picture hanging on the wall of a woman I knew, a woman of the night, came alive. The portrait of her face began to turn and move as I stared with great emotion and intense concentration. I somehow got her attention and told her that she was just as crazy as I was. She tried to deny it, but I stared at her hard intensely. As I looked at her, I realized that we both came from Egypt and had reincarnated.

I was with the wife of another man; she was showing me some art in a special place. I began to touch her breasts when she showed me this art. We had to leave this place, but as we went outside to go down the steps, you could not see the stairs. The place was as tall as a skyscraper; from one angle you could see the steps, from the top you could not. Finally, we made it out of the building in our separate ways. The woman went into a room at the bottom of the building; when I tried to go in, some women stopped me and said she would meet me later.

I said hello to Aunt Clara twice. While I thought about Mom's transition, on the second time, she said hello. However, I noticed that she was very light skinned and beautiful. Her eyes were very haunting and piercing. The other young woman wanted to ride with me. There was also a little girl with Aunt Clara.

CALVIN EARL DALLAS

I was looking for a pay period, another came and I noticed that the bathroom, Miss Ca left was messed up with her project, so I cleaned it up. Then I noticed all the water being let out was red, going to the city. I was in a swimming pool, and a boy dropped his toothbrush.

He was very high up. A beautiful woman, who was about to swim, said she would take it to him. As I left the pool, someone made a bet. That someone came in the pool and put three checks down on it. They were all personal checks on the book. The book fell into the water, but we recovered it. There was a man, who I had seen before, threatening another man, who had put all his money on the bet. I told this man to be quiet; the other threatening man smiled. Even though they had no clothes on, I took to a spot that was safe in the complex. I found that they had murdered the people in the tower. So I told them to stay in this room; it had a kind of sucklewall. One of the man got frightened because he saw on the other side his assassin. However, the assassin could not get to him.

I was in a room that I was not supposed to go into; I was tall like a giant. There was a little girl in the room lying on a bed, reading a paper. I called her a name that I thought might be hers; she corrected me and gave me her name. In addition, when I looked closely at the document she was reading, it had my name on it. It seemed to be some type of certificate. As I looked closer, I became aware that I was like a giant. I talked to the girl, but she would not look at me when I talked to her. Her nails were very long. I noticed that she never changed her position. I asked her if she was human. Of course, she did not reply.

I was at church and some more teachers and I were organizing many children. It seemed as though they were watching a movie.

A group of painters transported their works of art by air and sea to other places for show and prizes. We apparently all came from the same school of learning. The law cadets tried to stop us from pursuing our dreams. I stared at one very long and hard; I could feel and see that I had more power than the other artist did. I wanted to protest the matter. I knew this was not my style, and it seemed that my works of art had been stolen.

There was a house on the beachfront; apparently, someone had not finished building it. I was sleeping in an abandoned unfinished house. I was sleeping on the floor; as I got up, I noticed that there was construction going on not too far from the house. There were various machines used to clear the land. A white tourist family came to the house and said they needed a place to stay. I said, "This is nobody's house, I am just sleeping here on the floor, so I do not see why you cannot stay here."

They were very thankful. They filled up the refrigerator with groceries; they stayed in two rooms in the house. Next came my two sisters, Loraine and Barbara; they wanted to stay with me also. I told them that they could stay downstairs where I was sleeping. I talked to Loraine outside the house about how I had dreamed this. She talked to me about her dreams and everything; the whole experience was so real and clear. When I was inside again with Loraine and Barbara, a little friendly puppy had messed on the floor, so I threw him out of the house and cleaned the mess up. I told my sisters he was coming back, and he did, so I rubbed his face into the floor where he had made the mess. As I walked around the house, it seemed to be more complete. The tourists had gone into their rooms; I did not want to bother them. I noticed from the outside, the house looked more modern and complete. I looked at the beachfront, and the machines seemed to be still at work I had met some entities, and they would not leave me alone. They were very sticky when they touched me. I would tear their bodies apart into pieces. I had told them to leave me alone.

I was at a table with a group of women eating a certain dish, then I noticed the dish of food was gone. I asked them if someone had taken the food and they said no, but after a while, I saw that the food was hidden under the tablecloth, right in front of me. I must have lost consciousness or awareness at the movement when someone hid the food under the tablecloth.

I was in a place where there were all black women who were helping me in an office, then there was quiet.

I was in a bustling city, never seen before. A tall man from a construction site came over to show me around. He was very affectionate and warm to assure my comfort in the new place. Apparently, others were there too. It seemed to be time to go back and everyone had to get on this ship. However, there was an explosion on the ship; I could see the black smoke.

The landscape was of sand, and I shoveled a crease in the hill of sand, as to make my mark. Some other man told me to stop, but I did not. Next thing I knew, I was in another city that I had never seen before: people, transportation, all looked new. However, the main thing was that I was cool, calm, and very focused. In another place, I was moving some wine bottles. My principal was watching me, then my supervisor took one of the wine bottles away and said with several efforts, while he and another man watched me, "You are a wine expert." I asked my principal if I should move the shelf to the other side, and she said yes. I noticed it seemed to take a long time to pick up a wine bottle.

I was in projected awareness, and I was teaching an aikido class. I met with my sensei. I was merry, and my wife went with me. There was a little girl dressing in the dojo. I had taught some techniques and was taking a break when I noticed I had my martial arts uniform on strangely.

I was on a bus traveling to another city; I had my horn and I was playing it. While on the bus, there were also other people on the bus. I noticed there were two young men sitting behind me who did not get off the bus when it was time to debark. They whispered that they intended to ride the bus to the end of the line. There was a young man who had a room with a bed ready for me in this city. The real city of destination was on the other side of this one. In this room were a nice bed and a picture calendar of a pretty woman. He said I should go and see her movie and that it was scary. However, the woman looked pretty, and this person seemed to know me.

My aikido sensei said that he would give classes the next day in the afternoon. The classes would be free. I was very happy because of the great amount money I had found in the mailbox. My friend had left the change for me after buying something at the store for me. I had grabbed the money up and brought it to a room where all the members of my group were living. Even though I had all this money, they were emotional; they were arguing about their feelings. I let them know that I planned to share the money with them. I also told my sensei say that I went to the hospital to visit my friend from Trinidad that's why I did not make it to the aikido class. My sensei was light skinned and very much alert; he seemed to be studying something.

I had a dream in a room; Mom was there, then I shared my room and clothes with my brother, James. He changed the room slightly and arranged the bookshelves and TV differently. Next thing I knew, it was flooding outside the building. The water was very deep, almost up the hill. I tried to go around the apartment. Finally, I couldn't get to the apartment. I wound up hanging from some type of object. What it was, I didn't know. Finally, I found myself trapped in a room. Someone was ripping the room open; at that point, I saw that there were two dogs in the room with me that I didn't see before. When I got out of the room, the people left quickly, so I didn't get to see them. I found myself talking to someone about opening up a tai chi class at the Inner City Arts Council.

I played a game and got a number two lock for a prize.

Put a steel bar with two loops at the end of it under or inside of a swimming pool, which was filled up with water.

I actually visited my mother, watched TV with her, then she swept the floor with the broom. She had a black gown on, and she looked great.

I was on a farm, I had my own house, and I was making a collage, with a beautiful woman.

I saw some rates. I knew one had three dogs. One of the dogs jumped on me and started doing something to my hand. What it was I couldn't tell.

I could feel my body come back into my regular body naturally and very lightly.

I went to a restaurant to eat. There were many different restaurants in one place with people, but I went to an oriental one, and a familiar face sat next to me. Next thing I knew, I was outside in a country that was vast and beautiful. Sitting at the same table across the way was my sister Lorene, and some other familiar faces sat at a table not too far away. Some other young ladies at my table looked at me closely. Finally, I got up and two other guys sat at my table with playing cards. I had the same cards. I was going to use some to pay for my dinner, in fact, and I seemed to know these guys. Lorene called out to me from her table. I wanted to go to her but didn't. One of the guys at our table got up and started walking around, talking, and chain-smoking. I thought, He *is smoking too much.* Then all of a sudden, I looked around and he had left and, on a rock or bag, had left a note that he would be back.

I talked a while to the other fellow at the table, then I made my way inside the mountain. Of course, I seemed to be inside a cave. I saw young men walking on air very fast, high in the sky, planting some type of seeds in heaven. I wondered how they could do that. I called out to them, "Celestial farmers, celestial farmers," but they didn't hear me. They seemed to be in another dimension, planting seeds on heavenly air. I looked closely at their feet. They stepped across the skies, planting seeds in heaven. After seeing this, I realized I had to get out of the cave. I crawled down, nude, from a large rock that I had been on to the outside.

I told my friend at the table outside what I had seen. He said that I had to go home and eat and see our parents. As we walked, I told him of how this would be a great place to raise a family; he agreed. But I asked what about the winters; he said don't worry about that. We got back and knocked on the door we found. A heavy white woman was sitting on a heavy white man; they seemed to my parents or some relatives. They were mostly fat, and I looked at them straight in their eyes. As I washed my hands, the lady came close to me. I could feel her energy.

He was in a costume, then all of a sudden, it came off. He was dark skinned in a suit, young looking, but he could not stay on the ground; he would levitate at intervals. Other people were watching him also. Everyone went back.

Even though they had no clothes on, I took him to a safe spot in the complex. I found out that they had murdered the people in the tower. I told him to stay in a room that had a clear deco-type of glass wall. One of the other men that I hid got frightened because he saw an assassin on the other side, but the assassin did not see him. He panicked more and more and ran very fast around in circles on the walls of the room. I finally woke up.

The woman was beautiful; she showed me the forest that she planned from a little to now a thousand of auras.

I went to the restaurant, and I saw some woman cooking food in the back. I was with Al, talking to another brother who was very lean and close to me.

We were riding bikes and the young woman went to Aunt Clara's house to leave her bike there.

I was in a great disco, and everyone was dancing. I left the disco. I walked around the campus and saw mixed couples and lots of girls. Barbara, along with my mother and other family members, gave me a big bag of money. People walking by were looking, so I took the bag under my arm and headed for my room. Upstairs from the disco, my brother was afraid to come in, but I told him to. There were more people dancing in the disco.

The woman was walking; she also was smoking. She saw him and, with a touch of a finger on his face, sent him flying over a house in the air; she went too. They were found hanging from a telephone post in midair, unconscious.

I was looking around at a university house, but something happened. Everyone seemed to go off walking vertically in the air and disappearing into another dimension. I called the name of Jesus to get them back. They did come back. Then the setting changed; we were in a church. There were various people there. One woman said that she had always admired me, so she said a poem to me. For some reason, I felt a little uneasy. I tried to sit down in that place, the church, but something felt not right. I went to the bathroom. I saw there were a group of young men who were trying to go to that dimension again, and they were generating high vibrations with almost an acid rock-type of intense music. They all were very much aware of me. One called to me, "Hey, Albert, nice to see you again."

I told him that my name was Calvin Dallas, and he just said, "Oh." I had some books hidden inside of the back of my pants when the woman said the poem to me. I asked the light-skinned woman would she call me and stay in touch with me since we liked each other so much.

I was an Egyptian pharaoh in a sarcophagus, but I arose out of the casket to the light because I didn't want to be shut in and locked up; my consciousness was still awake and alive.

I dreamed I was in a restaurant buying strawberry ice cream. I was in a city where I knew some of the people, but I ventured out and they brought me back on the bus.

I was at a gathering with one serving of food, then a gentleman brought some very large pizzas. He gave me a knife to cut one piece, but he said I could take the whole pizza, so I did. I put it on the table while I ate.

The others I took to another table outside or to another location. When I came back to the gathering, I noticed everything was different; the group of men were focused on something else, so I went back to get the pizza and the children had eaten it up. There were a few pieces left. I took them. I saw one girl who was one them who had eaten the pizza. I grabbed her hand. She told me to let go or her mother would cut my neck, so I let her go.

I was fighting with a group of people with yin pressure points to collapse the body. I woke up when they pressure-pointed me.

—✳—

I was working with the police in training their recruits in shooting and self-defense.

I met a white lady in a carnival. I spun around in a circle with her; next thing I knew, she covered me with her dress. I felt her heart center radiate through me.

We made love, but I didn't come. I used sexual kung fu, and she made me feel good. I followed her to her place where there were so many other pretty ladies.

I was with a great light-skinned lady, who lived in another island. I was close to her. I told her about seeing a lost lion and tiger walking freely at the entrance of her island. I kissed her, and for a long time, her tongue seemed to be sticky, but she enjoyed it, then some young boy came out of nowhere and hit m. I asked her who he was; she said she didn't want to get into it. I told her about how I met her, then I kissed her for that long time, and I also told her I wrote it down. She gave me the keys to her place, but other people were there too.

There was a castle, but it leaked with water. It was Linda at the door to stop me, and I told her it wasn't fair.

I saw myself come back into the room, but not into the body, after the astral journeys. I rode in a cart like car down the stairs through buildings.

I was finally in a town where the people were very friendly to me. They brought me every dish, and I ate; after, they asked me how I liked it. One lady said I didn't have to pay right away. I was totally grateful, but I did pay. Some excitement broke loose after I had eaten. Someone black was chasing someone down the street, and another person was running with a camera, trying to film it.

It seemed that consciously I was aware of more than one level at a time. One lady said I should buy a sports T-shirt.

I was thinking and focusing on a certain amount of money constantly; it was almost like my mind kept seeing me or a lady having this amount, over and over again.

First, I projected out of my body state. I was in the classroom situation with other people or persons who seemed to be a man talked to us in a very instructional voice, while there was another computer or a mechanical voice that was very low and male. It suggested that initiatory of government existed in the future and that you could be executed for not following coordinates. A picture was shown of a male spitting fire and smoke, as it screamed in terror of power and dominance. All the time in the class, I wanted to ask questions, but there seemed no place in his or the instructor's agenda for questions; the female's role of kindness had been left out.

I was on a large bus similar to a Greyhound Bus. Everyone was wondering why the bus didn't take off yet, so I went into the other side of the bus. The bus had been moving, but it stopped. It seemed that there was a driver exchange. I saw the new driver; he wore dark shades and was black and very introverted. Quickly, he read my mind and said that he was early, then all of a sudden, he got up and got into the driver seat and started driving the bus. It was totally empty on one side and the other side was full. I decided to go to the front of the bus and sit where there was no driver. I tried to understand how this bus was moving on the highway when there was no one in front driving. Then I realized this bus was driven by the driver in the back. I was thinking, *I better get to the part of the bus where the people were,* then I heard a voice mail say, like from an intercom system, that the bus was going to detach, and it did. The part I was in was detached and left on the side of the road, while the main full part of the bus kept moving. All of a sudden, a tall young white man showed up on a motorcycle and said that he would try to catch the bus. But that he could go faster with me riding with him. I remember the bus was headed to Hartford. But now, I was in a small town with hardly any clothes on. I walked up a hill to a church of a monumental building that a lot of people were in. I looked out for the police. When the people came out, they didn't seem to mind me. I saw one little child's finger was injured by another little child. I talked to this child. There was also a man that I talked to about my problem; he told me about a catastrophe at sea. I noticed that the people didn't make it seem strange that I was there.

My oldest brother was taking care of children; his wife wanted me to work hard, but the work of bringing the children's artwork up had already been completed.

I saw myself almost crumble up a drawing in a room where there was an instructor. I went to the bathroom to wash my hands and then tore some paper towels off a utensil to dry my hands. When I came back to the room, a student who was doing a drawing complimented me on the drawing that I was doing, so I said thank you. I also complimented him on the drawing he was doing. His drawing seemed to be a vehicle in the sky, and my drawing seem to be different. I could see the drawings clearly.

I was at a table talking to some people, and I noticed two young ladies walking in my direction: one was very hip-hop and sassy, the other one, when she got close to me, was short and had soft warm brown skin. She came slowly close to me and kissed me gently on my lips with her full lips, then both of them walked away slowly. I talked to some man about a famous book.

I protected the girl; she was cream colored, with soft blue loving eyes, and a slim shape. She took me to a woman's house, possibly her mother. The lady told me to come in and take my shoes off. She kneeled down to pray, but she wanted me to go back outside to get a monkey. All I saw and felt was that I was walking on the hard ground with no shoes on, and there was a car with two bright blinking red lights, just sitting there, waiting for someone. It was nighttime.

We were being attacked by vampires, but finally, they left. One light-skinned girl was being attacked but survived; the house seemed safe.

The man said the dirt was getting softer in the world. I saw him knocking down walls of concrete. I asked him, "Didn't they need to put steel in the walls?" His reply was that he said steel in another language, then he left. Two men came and set off explosives. I ran, then I came back to that part of the building that had exploded.

I looked for my shoes and found a couple of pairs, but the black cowboy boots had been stolen. Some of my clothes had been cleared out for another gentleman who was staying in the same house, but there was one garment that was oriental left for me to wear. It was very long and unique. The room that the woman stayed in was blocked off; there was only one way in.

There was a jealous girl or lady because my mother made me a cake, so she put a fingernail lock on my hand, but it was triple the force of the lock on her hand, she cried.

I was in my home, then water came in from cooking a pot of food. I mopped it up. There seemed to be neighbors coming around.

A beautiful lady, who looked like a Malaysian woman, drove me around in a fast sports car. I showed her the ocean and the beaches. She rubbed my leg with her foot. A large woman got jealous and told the Malaysian-looking woman that she was just showing off. The large woman picked up a document out of the car and left the Malaysian-looking woman. The Malaysian woman seemed upset; she called after the large woman several times, "Auntie!"

There was a blonde woman who had a friend who kept falling asleep. In an important ceremony, she kept her awake, then when she got back home, a lot people wanted me to look at her and greet her, but when I did, she was with another man enjoying herself. I made a mistake and spilled some drink with a strong stain. She looked at me and was pleased, then she and her boyfriend went somewhere else. I showed the Malaysian woman the pictures on my cell phone of many subjects, racing cars on a high canyon road, and sports.

A white man rode through a camp with a mounted machine gun in his topless car; he looked very stern and protective.

I saw a lady by herself quietly looking at some documents while there was a party going on downstairs. I could have gone to the party or talked to the lady. I was aware of both events at the same time. I was mainly focused on the lady while hiding so she wouldn't see me.

I was playing a game of tennis in a stage with a young lady; there were a few other people in the scene. Then I was giving an art class; they were drawing from famous books of art.

Me and a lady, who was my lady, washed clothes in the basement of my parents' house, then I decided to hang them outside on the line. We went outside, and all the time, she communicated with me.

Somehow in this dream, we had stolen a whole cruise line ship. There were a lot of passengers on the ship. We sailed to a particular city, then sailed to another city. There was a father who chased his son on the ship. You could actually feel the boat go through the ocean or water; on land, it adopted wheels.

My father was in my dream. He was getting ready to go out, and I had a very neat apartment that we lived in, but I had a strange musical instrument that I couldn't get any sound out of.

I kept pulling a thread of skin off my foot; at first, it hurt, then I noticed the second time I did it, it didn't hurt so bad.

There was a woman waiting for me to be with her, but I didn't. Also, the priest told me to hurry up and I didn't. I wound up with hardly any clothes on, talking to some fellow who was my friend.

I heard Dr. E talk to Mrs. Farrow about an incident. I thought he was retired, but it seemed to be important.

A pretty young lady was drunk; I tried to help her get better.

I rode a motorcycle to and from a party in a city.

I kept seeing fat ladies and tried not to curse them, but I kept hearing a voice come out of my head. I had to sign in.

The man wanted to take my suit, but I would not let him.

The Russians were taking over, so we were developing an army.

They were all invited to a meeting for martial artists; one passed me by on a bicycle. He said he would talk to me later.

I was with some beautiful girls; the light-skinned one whom I had a relationship with talked to me. We had been trapped in a house because something outside was not right.

There was a long alligator in the room, and we couldn't get out. I told everyone that it was a psychological experiment or trap, so I went to the underground level and saw the nursery. The lady in charge was protected by a special see-through glass like a force field. She called the authorities. I saw little children sleeping quietly, then I noticed someone from an aerial blast out of a building, influencing a group of people to go back in a city area. I think it was the authorities.

We attracted the ladies at the club, but they led us into a trap, where the Russians were acting like women and we had to get away.

The two dogs were a gray-blue color; they jumped on me in a tree. One liked me, but his skin was kind of smooth, not hairy; I could see it was a male, but the other dog liked me too. They both followed me, then I saw a man who was afraid of them. He was trying to get to their house. Next thing I heard some woman saying that I had killed the dog. I went to the lady's house and told her she was wrong. I told her the dog probably liked me and that the other man had killed it; she cried loudly.

I saw green snake-like creatures go into a wall; the rest turned into skinny rope-like creatures, but I was high up on a ladder; they couldn't get to me.

Linda's sister had my cell phone. They performed in a church; a lady, a white minstrel type, led me to a church. I asked her how she knew I was looking for a church. She didn't quite tell me, but the church was huge and vast with thousands of doors. Finally, she told me which one to go in. I saw that I was in the right place. There was a group of men that I sat with; they seemed to be ministers, and some were watching babies. After they sung, I could take good pictures with the old camera I had. After they sung, I went to the place where their fans waited for them. It took a long time before they came out, but she sent me something to read, and it said to get the camera tomorrow, but I wanted it today. I grabbed and I snacked; one of her messengers came out again and said she would see me. Linda came out with a blonde wig on and finally gave me my phone that her sister had.

Three men were running; they wanted money, but I said I took up a chair to protect myself from one who had a weapon.

I was underground. I had to leave but had clothes on different pipes.

The swinging in different people, places, and running in this New City.

In a dream, I cut my hand; a lot of people looked under the skin at the cut. I held my hand with my other hand so that I couldn't bleed so much.

I held a life form in my hands with black hair, rat or mouse like, but not human like, but it seems to come from an entity or being that is female humanoid. The baby or life form is taut and round, full of energy and moved constantly in my hands, but didn't seem to make a sound.

The lady said she is with me, not her man, and another lady friend of mine said okay.

Mrs. Lastly was helping as teachers signed in for payroll; Mr. C was there.

I prepared a dish of food with fruits and vegetables in a creative style.

The boy couldn't figure out the addition process on the hand computer, so he scratched my face with his hand. I put him off, also scratching his face. He seemed to be asleep.

The large race went on along. Some runners fought and fell down; one lady started a fight with another lady. I started to run, but I saw some children and started to walk with them. I held one baby for the mother, and she was very happy. I saw that my mother wanted to shop and the mother wanted to close up shop of the baby I carried and loved.

—m—

In the dream, I met a woman whom I tried to guess her profession. She gave me an object to take to my place of living, and she was white and pretty.

I was leaving a building, and an airplane flew so close to me that I laid down on some steps.

I was in a session with a tai chi master. I asked him a question, "Does chi or energy enter the target before you touch it or while you think about it?" "Yes," he said.

Everyone had brought something to eat in a package; mine was on the refrigerator in a brown paper bag. The tai chi master was smiling all the time; there were many people there.

I saw a pink fluorescent unicorn, very small, and I tried to touch it; at first, it was frightened, then it became friendly. I had a great feeling as I touched it. It felt soft, like an elastic rubber glass, then I finally moved it gently with my touch. It had brisk movements in a mirror. The boy looked like a small young child.

I saw clearly the two Donovans sitting together, talking intimately.

I saw two beautiful ladies of the night; one was shot by a man, then her friend took her to the hospital.

There were almost one hundred little girls who came to visit some ladies in the towers. I could see them, and they were all colors. Mrs. Lastly was helping to supervise them. They had entered my room, and one girl had picked up a book of mine. I had to yell at her to put the book down and get out of my room.

I was in a car with Ted. We talked about Spanish people and people in general. He seemed to be much younger and clearer in the face. He and I talked about the origin of Spanish people.

There are many lights; green is cool. Now I have forgotten white moon, fire water, twinkling ambers that refresh my soul, angel standing by heaven, awake, hearts of softness, smiling babies, dreams of genius.

The warmth, stillness tranquil heights, fragrances of delight, soaring in flight, cosmic sights, mystic chilling.

The night chimes in red from distant might. New horizons in the air transcends golden rays of love. Ancestors tight, green, yellow, bright and shimmering sunsets in galaxies' purple night.

She smiled knowingly. Beauty enchantment, emerald's cold palace, heavens delight, diamonds inside dancers of merry-go-rounds, swaying gracefully bound in rhythms to be found. Purple, crimson, brown, sky lights heaven bound, to transcendental town, *boom*, *bang*. Hold nothing with everything round.

Where does the dream begin? It begins in the spiritual world. Development and enhancement take place in the physical world. As the dream grows more and more, new perception is developed, and as a result, the cosmic or eternal energy throughout infinity is gathered, stored, and circulated, just as the sun replenishes itself constantly, sharing its energy with other celestial bodies.

My journeys in my dreams have been as though I am awake in the same place as when I go to sleep.

One night, I dreamed I tried to untangle necklaces from around my neck. I wanted help because I became strangled.

Another night, I dreamed that I was trying to walk around in my room. In these two dreams, I felt a vibration before they occurred. In one dream, I saw a girlfriend sleeping next to me with a white light leaving her body. As I viewed this light, it sounded like someone was reciting a prayer. I put my hand through the white light, trying to stop it from coming out of her. I saw a friend of hers looking into the window at us. I wanted to open the door for him, but she said it's okay.

A dream can be so real.

I think it was Duke Ellington, but then he looked like Monsanto's husband. They came into the basement where I was making these awards and said, "Yeah, forget the women and do the honor to the men all right. There a picture of your father. Yeah, he was like that."

He said, "I am going to see the film, the *Black Gods.*"

I said, "Is it here?"

He said, "It's in Atlanta, but it's going to be here."

Then he gave me something, an award; it was round, white, and blue. It said, "To an all-around martial artist."

He looked at me a while and then said, "Remember."

As I looked at it, a picture flashed in my mind. Then he laughed greatly, also then he said, "Win the next time. I'll pour you a glass of my finest vintage," then he left. Apparently, he knew my father.

I was on a bus ride. I came off the bus to soon. I was lost. I don't know why I came off the bus so soon. A lady was riding a bicycle; she wanted to give me a ride. But someone was on the bike already, sleeping. So she was just going to show me the way when we got to the other station. They asked me why did I come off the bus. I really didn't know; all I know is I lost some money in a red container lunch box, and there was an old man pushing an old lady in a wheelchair. When we got to the other station, her bike went down the triangle slope; the old lady pushed the old man down the slope, and the wheelchair hit the old lady who had ridden the bike in the heel. I asked her if she was all right. I was woken up by women's voices that said, "It's not too far off."

I showed a man by the name of James, a white man, how to block a punch and kick. My mother was also showing this man some tai chi and how to use the energy in a swirl block. She did it beautifully. I told these people how they could tell, by the markings on the uniform's left shoulder, what degree he had mastered. There was a large crowd of people watching the events.

James had to leave. So I also left. I saw a man pick up a black onyx jewel ring, and I looked at it very closely. There were two pieces; one had a very intricate design on it.

I had a dream that I was explaining to someone that I was a Christian.

I had a dream that there was a voice telling me to run faster.

The first dream was where some people or associates made some strange sculpture pieces under my directions.

The next dream was a shootout in which some other boys were trying to destroy a family with guns. A little girl got in the way, but her mother helped her out of the way.

I visited some places where my father gave me a lot of inspiration. He bought a lot of groceries; I noticed a lot of canned fruits and vegetables. It really looked like a lot of food. I wanted to steam some rice. I had all the equipment. My sister Lorene was there too.

I saw Father; he asked me was I studying about people from other planets. I said yes hesitatingly.

I saw Brenda in a dream. Yes, she was afraid of me and screamed. I had my father's coat on.

My father and I talked about waterproof shoes. Then we looked at some astrology charts and stars closely in the heavens; there was someone else there. Then some outer space being gave me something very quick in a very colorful box. The next morning, I woke up, and I felt great.

After the concert, I put on a wide-span multicolor hat and a colorful cape. I felt unique and different, and though everyone was probably not looking at me, I did it because I felt like it because it was classic. During the concert, the featured musician played at the top and the bottom of a string guitar-like instrument with both hands. As he plucked the strings simultaneously, the melodies sounded like a symphony in jazz. One time while he was playing from the stage, he looked directly into my eyes and said to save the children in gangs several times.

I was in a neighborhood that I could not get out of. I was trapped like a subject in a maze. I kept walking down the same streets and passing the same houses, like in a rectangular box but not a circle.

I was running in the street in the dark night; close behind was a slim young woman who was riding a motorcycle with very bright taillights. The finally the young lady asked me to ride with her. We rode to various sections of the city. She stopped and two young men got into the motorcycle, which had the space. To me, they seemed to be her two brothers; they were very young. She said nothing to them and they said nothing to her. Later on, I asked her if they were her brothers, and she said yes.

CALVIN EARL DALLAS

Running in a beautiful green park with my brother, I could see tranquil ponds of clear dark water, a refreshing feeling.

A mysterious lady wrote her identification on some paper out of a notebook that I had. She took more paper than she needed and wouldn't give them back. But she didn't want me to know who she was, so I told her about it, and she just said goodbye and take care.

This dream, I was in a truck or vehicle with another or more people. We seemed to be descending down across several highways, like from the top of a hill or mountain. The feeling was as if we were falling onto different lower highways. We drove for a while on one and then went to the next. In the end, everything was okay.

Out of the liquid, I picked up a smiling baby. The light-skinned man tried to get away from the baby. I knew that it was his, and I caught him on the circuit pattern. He wanted to know what I had for him, a few pieces of paper, and he ran away quickly when I showed him his baby. He never came back. I saw a vision of racing cars colliding.

My father asked about the pyramid. He seemed a bit confused. I told him that one was warmer and the other was colder. His body seemed to be in good shape.

A little girl showed me how to walk on air and go through walls while her parents watched too. Her father fell and broke his leg while following me, as I was leaving. From very high up, they lived in a house several thousand feet up. After he fell, he came out of his body. I told him to go and tell his wife that his leg was broken.

I met a beautiful woman and her family from Egypt. I tried to stay with them but lost them. I took a picture with her. Out of the dark, something was chasing me and wouldn't stop. As I entered the light, I saw that it was a little girl; she was very pretty. Her event hit me now. I was in a place that had several rooms for entertainment. I left to find the woman. As I was outside throughout the town, I noticed that the dogs didn't bother me. I came back to the place of entertainment. At the very end, I saw the lady inside with her woman friends. I walked through the walls to come to her, but she didn't see me. I picked up some orange yarn and threw it on the table next to her. She still didn't notice me. So I decided to come through the door, but when I did, she had disappeared with her friends from sight. I knew I had to go back to the beginning and come to her. As I passed through the different rooms of entertainment, I saw many people, some women, children, and men, but it seemed as if I was connected with all of them. As I got ready to go from the beginning to the end, a brother stopped me and asked me for forty. He advised me to seek medical assistance. I told him I knew where I wanted to go. So I gave him the money, and soon after that, I woke up.

I was with my father's father; he looked great coming from an apartment. I bought ice cream and ice crystals from a certain woman's store.

I levitated through a neighborhood; people watched. I had the power by just holding the level of awareness. I had fun going way up and traveling horizontally as well. Leslie's wife hugged and kissed me in a dream to congratulate me on stopping him and another person from fighting.

I was riding a bicycle and had a strange hat on with two objects; I threw them off. A wife and husband discussed dinner. A stoplight was in effect. I stopped then the whole family got on my back, and they were white, including the children. I rode as fast as I could, then they got off.

I gave out supplies at a school that only had a few classes in a section. The same woman was there in a particular ironing room, where I rode on the bicycle.

The time jump into the future was by one year. A woman in the Golden Brotherhood kissed me. She was very direct and then I shot into another world. I was flying, then I saw a new city from a vehicle in the air. The city had golden pyramids and other unique buildings. As I went into the station, the brothers from the Golden Brotherhood advised me and watched me to make sure I could handle the jump. I felt like crying some of the time, but I handled the jump. I was informed that I was a player with a brand-new car.

This was a night with the most beautiful woman I have ever been with; we worked together on several cycles of kung fu. She stopped for an herbal substance, and I saw some young man enter into the next room. I looked at him out of the door. She said she only wanted me. Her figure was outstanding, and physically and spiritually, she was very beautiful. We both held each other closely together. Her love was magnifying.

I healed a family with terrible scars. Scar spots of red blood and yellow crust were there. I put a white sheet over my head and went into a room by myself. I noticed that the sheet started to turn yellow. So I called on my inner powers and took the white cloth off. I looked into the mirror and saw the brown melanin sheet. I knew that I wasn't sick, even though his children were touching me. I realized this was his family and that he had given me a ride in a strange long car. When I first got in, it seemed to have not that much room, just for me and him. I was lost in the dream, trying to get to a place to do tai chi. The next thing I knew, the car had a blacktop and someone was sitting behind me. Finally, we arrived at his place. I saw that all the people there had some type of blood and yellow disease on their body. I realized it was his family. When I had the white cloth over my body, I started to see yellow come through, then I got nervous. Some inner power changed it back to white. Then I took off the white cloth and saw only my shiny brown skin. As I went into the other room, I noticed that the skin of all the children and the person who brought me was different; it was kind of a light cream color, with a tinge of yellow in it. Everyone was healed just by my little movement in the other room. Not knowing a display in front of them, a yang movement of kung fu. All of a sudden, everyone went outside; I realized that a spaceship had come to pick them up. Before I ran outside to see the spaceship, I had to find my shoes. I saw one pair, but it wasn't mine. I looked further and saw another pair, and they were mine. As I grabbed the shoes, I ran to go out, and one of the doors was locked, so I busted the door down. I heard the wind; someone was talking, then as I got outside, I saw the most amazing technology: a circular ship, metallic silver of some sort. I could see through the metal; several prongs came out of the ship's body, like pointed spider legs, to pick these children and people up. There were people inside of the prongs with some type of computer. I got inside the ship; one of the women of the crew spotted me as not one of them, and somehow, I convinced her to let me enter further. Then I met a woman robot, who tried to stop me, but as I touched and sung patterns, she didn't compute it. It was hard for her to stop me. There were also two other women, who were either human or robots, who liked me; they were part of the people who were taken up in the spaceship.

I was trying to catch flying insects in the family's house. With a round pot, I finally caught some. But when I was going to destroy them, they changed into two black children. I found my father and asked him what to do. We kept them in the family's house.

I was doing a tai chi class in a dojo when another martial artist came flying in the air over to me; he was light skinned and very strong, with inner strength. I seemed to know him.

I ran through a natural country to a town or city where the people wanted me to wait the next day before I ran again. The runway through the forest and grassland was very long.

Ladies and men, we were moving basically items, mostly furniture, in an underground passage. I remember me telling some women not to tell me where to go or what to do.

A lady gave me a liquid to drink; she asked me if it tasted like wine or champagne. I told her it tasted like neither because it had no taste.

I dreamed I was at a university. I was concerned about my degree, I visited my mother. I wanted to fix the falsity, but my mother said, "Keep praying to Jesus." In the dream, I felt I could do it myself.

I dreamed that I had a fast car. I was trying to fix it, and it was running or the motor would start by itself.

I was in a strange house. A little girl came to the door. I pressed a button, and I saw the little girl through a rectangular window in the door; at the same time, I heard the wind blowing hard. I looked down and under the floor; there was another dimensional space.

I ran a great run in a place where I was known by a couple of great women. After the race, I tried to get together with these women, but they seemed to be not interested in me as a friend. So I traveled the countryside and found a lot of pleasure in admiring nature's beauty.

I dreamed I was with a group of people who were playing dead. We had to jump into an area that seemed like a resting place. There were scientists there; they told us not to move. But there was a lady, a beautiful one, who started to kiss me. We were very much alike. The next thing I knew, I was out of the situation.

Now there's another character that was in a show, and there were a lot of people there. Then he went to another show and there were a lot of people there, but there was one girl who continued to sit by him. She was a redhead and looked slim and attractive. The people around this character were very friendly; there was a type of abstract music playing. Some people had dogs for pets. One person asked if anyone had cookies.

Next thing I know, this character was going to a disco. As he entered, he went through the hallway and up some very long stairs. It seemed I had never been there before; the people there were mainly white, and upstairs where the character sits were a lot of blacks. One told me that someone was coming to knock me off. Two old men came in, one at an angle and one in the back. The one in the back took out his weapon. I took out something to protect myself, a round chair. Then I jumped out the window. The way down was very long, but by the time I got down, I was okay but very distant from my body. A van picked me up. The famous person in the van jumped in. I was off in the distance. I traveled in a moment to the van, and inside, I was telling the character that it was time for him to go home to his wife. Than all of a sudden, he was not there anymore. I asked the van driver if I'm the character, and he said, "What do you think?"

I looked out the van window at all the unfamiliar roads, wondering how to get back to my wife. I felt lost. I told the van driver I'm lost, then all of a sudden, there appeared a beautiful lady, who was not dressed up. She gave me directions. I cried and said, "May a thousand blessings fall upon you."

She told me, "Likewise."

There was a part in the dream where men dressed like women, danced together, and one tried to entice me, but I held him off.

I went back to the playground to find my 16mm Bolex camera. After seeing two people who were very cold, I brought my friend some musical instruments. When I got to the playground, the same musical instruments were stacked in a neat pile. There were many students of a strange drunken nature on the playground. I told them not to touch the instruments. They were angry and started throwing sticks at me, which I seemed to know would hit me, so I ran away from the playground slowly. They still taunted me by yelling and throwing sticks. Finally, I told them that I was just looking for my camera, which I had loaded the wrong way in the light. The next thing I knew, the group of students were calming down. A director or coordinator appeared and questioned me about the activity that I caused with his students. First, he greeted me, then I greeted him. He had a large body and very intent eyes. As he talked to me with some honor, his students all went into this building. Then he left.

The next thing I know, I was making a puppet move that was life-size. The puppet looked like a Raggedy Ann, but it turned into a kite. I flew her high in the sky, and she turned into a butterfly, then I brought her down and had her dance in the streets for a group of people. Then I flew her up in the sky as a human kite. I flew her very high and changed her again; some people got mad because I caused everyone to look at my kite instead of theirs. I couldn't see the string that held the kite; it was there but invisible. So I brought the kite down this time. I saw three nudes that I had control of. By this time, the crowd had grown very large. I brought the three nudes against the wall so that people could watch them; all of a sudden, I changed them into three pretty ladies, who obeyed my invisible string. And even though they moved as puppets, people still talked to them but kept moving on. All of a sudden, I made the women change to men. I controlled their movements also, with the invisible thread that never breaks.

Brothers were getting high, but I had stopped. They were getting high right in my parents' house. I saw I am not into this even though my brothers were.

I admired my sister very much; we went to dinner.

I went to house that had bars on every window, and the rooms and doors were locked. I went into one room, and it locked behind me, so I woke up the secret advisors telling me to study the process.

I was running naked through some city and other areas or parks or nature; a police-looking person talked to me, first one, then two. The person had a special uniform on. I put a sheet of a magazine or newspaper to cover my private area. I went through New York where they were selling drugs.

We were wrestling with different techniques.

I sat on a box, but there were other people there, and we had to wait our turn.

Some people were shooting guns at me, so I dropped down to the ground behind a car, then one came after me. I ran into a large brick stone building. I kept running up the stairs until I came out of the building where there was large fence behind the building.

I was high up on a ship and couldn't come down to a lower level, no matter what I tried.

She talked to me for a long time. She said, "So you don't want to eat and you don't know me."

I was in a bathroom in a strange city. The shit would float around in a liquid solution. Men chased me for money. Then I got a ray gun. But a friend didn't want me to use it. It was very powerful.

In the dream, I told my sister that I didn't exactly live the same lifestyle as her. As she put me out, I looked for a bus to get home and automatically woke up.

I went to a party. Some of the women wore masks. One lady was in charge. My orders were to make creative creations from what I was given. It seemed everything I had come up with, she had something to say about it. A lady was playing music with other musicians in the party. The woman gave a dance. I finished several creations. So I decided to play the trumpet. I walked around and waited for an opportunity but never got one. I felt very mystical.

My mother and I explored life forms. One looked very tiny and swirled in a bottle of liquid. It had two strands and plants; another life form was green, and it had been pulled out of a container that had liquid. It was next to a guardian. It looked like a flathead octopus, with no eyes, long tenable green legs, about eight. It tucked in its body when pulled out of water, then expanded as if contracted first. A little girl put up the container with the life form in it and carried it a little distance, then all of a sudden, dropped the container with the life form in it. My mother said, "Don't get mad at the little girl."

I tried to gather the soil and the plant life up with my hands, but couldn't. My mother and I observed that the life form was still alive, swirling only with one strand and adapting quickly to its new circumstances.

The tire said Silver Rider, and I was in a city where I was riding a bike to a paper-route place. The people there were waiting to see me. When I got there, one person said that he wanted to make some serious changes in the work program. We seemed to be inside, but there were no windows. I was looking at a boy. It didn't bother him, but I opened the windows from the outside; it seemed to be raining.

I was in a plane of learning with another man; we went out the building, and I sensed that the wind was howling and that it was very cold. There was a woman and a man looking at me. I didn't feel the cold physically, but I knew it was cold.

I created a 3-D painting of a woman who seem to be a model for me because only when she left did I notice that I was reproducing her in a painting. The painting seemed to be a 3-D sculptural piece of this lady.

I ran to a park and realized that the family reunion was at a house in the city. When I ran back to the house, I could hear James playing his horn. Everyone was in the backyard, and Leslie was inside, waiting for me to come in by him, but I went in a side where everyone respected me and honored me. One man seemed to start talking to someone on a walkie-talkie. When he saw me, I felt as if I was the one to make everything happen, and everyone knew it.

Several people were shot with an outside force, but still, there was a woman giving other women a bathroom. She was not shot and her patient wasn't shot. Then there was one other person in the bathroom, a man who wasn't shot. Outside of the house, there was a level of energy that seemed to be floating up, high in the air. I caught a flying bat that looked ancient and unusual. Then there appeared from the depths of the night a woman who looked like she was from another planet or dimension. She kept saying, "Let me eat in peace," but he kept following me. At one point, I directed her into a room where a sister of mine was. I told her to deal with my sister. But she continued to follow me; it seemed as though she was programmed.

Beautiful black woman, the universe twinkles in your hazel-brown eyes.

Right now, I also have many beautiful young ladies who love and care for me very much. They are just as rich as me and wise. These ladies allow me to love each one of them in my unique own way without hassle. My beauties are here and everywhere. I love to practice kung fu with these beauties. God knows that they make me feel good. A beautiful woman should be admired by every man for her charm, movements, and atmosphere. This is the reason why the world is at war because man has not realized or even took the time to treasure God's gifts, one of which is a woman. Man must realize that he comes physically into the earth through his mother. Who is his first contact with a beautiful woman? Through virtues, love, respect, honor, loyalty, freedom, truth, wisdom, and knowledge, man has his motherly inheritance. For some men, their first taste was their mother's milk. Some men spent their whole life looking for a woman who looks, acts, smells, and tastes good. wI was at a school of learning and was asked to sign a petition; as I signed the petition in cursive, I noticed all the letters were not totally shaped properly or correctly. The person who asked me to sign questioned me to the fact that maybe I might not be Calvin Dallas.

I saw a person look like a face with two holes in a rectangle. I asked, "If the master gave you two stones, would you give them to him?" The stones were very hot, so I took them too, and then a big machine took them from me. Then I saw a man destroy someone's home; other beings captured him. His one arm was locked into position with a saw-like tool, and his other arm was broken, but he was trying to put it in place. It seemed to be made out of a flexible liquid substance; finally after several tries, the arm was put into place with the saw-like tool.

I was wearing a great yellow suit with a cane or umbrella. Linda's sister saw me from her home window and said I looked great. The newspaper man told us that we shouldn't catch the bus because the weather was bad and it had been delayed.

I was in big mansion for a party. I was trying to figure out what suit to wear, and my sister helped me; she said red. Before the party, everyone was at the pool. I didn't swim too much because I wasn't a good swimmer in deep water, so I sat at the edge of the pool. There were two guys smoking, but I couldn't smell the smoke. So I got ready to leave, then I found out that a certain set of brothers had canceled the party because they wanted to charge money.

It was dark; I knocked out a man and took him downstairs. I was in a large bedroom with a curtain divided; the room was in front of the bed. Getting up, tying shoes on the bed, now two relatives of the man questioned me, then I went outside and saw a long road; it had yellow paint on it. Tony was walking down it with her face painted yellow.

I was in a place where people were shooting each other. My driver was shooting back, driving slow, telling me the story. I asked why people can't live in peace. I noticed there were no bullet holes in the car's front windows.

I traveled on the road in a car with Father. He went to another destination. I went to another point. He rested in bed.

In the city, there was conflict with guns used by people. I saw organisms change into other organisms. Then I saw them make new friends in the city.

11/25/05

IHAD A MYSTICAL DREAM of catching two black cats on a worm-infested rooftop. I gave one cat to a white man, another to a master. At first, I missed the first black cat by its furry tail; it glided through my hand. I could feel its fur, then it escaped into the worm-infested rooftop and then left. The next time, I grabbed the black cat by its tail. I felt its warmth and essence. I thought it would bite me, but it didn't, then a second black cat came back, and another master told me thanks and he took him.

The time was closing in. He had said that we had probably some mummies thousands of years ago, but now it was closed and sealed. Some tried to spray with some substance that changed the surface appearance. But the sprayer was bitten by a small deadly animal in the neck.

I saved a soldier, and a beautiful light-skinned lady hugged me for it. I talked and asked the young lady about Jesus, but the young lady didn't answer, I was in a beautiful home, and the young lady daughter called out to me.

I ate a raw type of pink egg at a table with other people. It tasted somewhat organic but smooth and a little tart.

I was in a place, my home; the phone rang, and there was a message left, then I picked up the phone. The connection was so bad that I couldn't penetrate or get my words through. But a lady had left a message. Her voice was so very soft. Then I wondered who she was. Not too long after that, the phone rang again. This time, I made sure that the cord in the phone was good. I wiggled it a couple of times, and here is what the lady said, "Have you ever had a woman counselor or woman talk to you about women?

I said no. Then she said we'll just get things out of the closet, and she would like very much to work with me. I said it sounded very interesting and I would like to hear more. Then she asked me if I got her first message, then I woke up.

I was in a place, like a park with hills, inside a closed area. A man hit a baseball with a bat at an object in the park, rocks, trees, or any natural solid object, so that the ball would be deflected to me in a very speedy way, of course. I was expected to catch it, which I did on one occasion, in which he said I would lose, so he was inspired to continue and test my ability with several balls coming toward me. Most of them I didn't catch, but I enjoyed this practice immensely. After we stopped, I told him he should train young children with this method. He called it the Green Leaf technique.

There was a woman who had something in her hair, and I got it out with some nail polish; she laid her head on my lap.

I was at some school, trying to find a good place to eat, when I realized I had passed the eating area.

I was talking to a woman very vividly.

I heard beautiful music, symphonic and erythematic beats, when I was out of my body.

Aunt Ti appeared and said she knew everything about me, then someone attacked me, and I woke up.

I saw some great insects that were life forms after my energy.

A group of people in a certain room were trying to destroy a snake with a certain cane; we succeeded, but I had to convince a certain being who the cane belonged to by force.

A group of people were in a bathing or swimming area, and the water was deep, but we were standing on high platforms. I took a shower with one girl, and she sexually tantalized me.

I was discussing the horizontal flow of an object with a coworker; it seemed like a lady coworker in television, but then the principal said it was the vertical and asked what about the horizontal. He said it's just a lot of confusion.

There was a group of certain beings. Then there was a female, taking leave of them, but before she left, she took an object from another being, with a thin white-looking wire. Then she got into a vehicle and nodded or bowed her head to him. As she went through the inside of the vehicle, she came to a door that leads to a certain room. She went in and removed her mask; her face had a very bad scar on it. Then she locked the door and she took up a clear sharp object and came toward me or someone; the next thing I realized or saw was a robot man waking up from a deep sleep. The woman with the scar on her face looked very healthy and pretty. The robot man can't believe this was him in the real world. Then as the spaceship passed over, a certain woman took a weapon and fired at these or this person who was sitting below in his dwelling, saying how dare she attack again. Out of his dwellings some object was hit. He said how dare she and her brother attack, then at the same moment, the robot was telling them to wait and stop. The next thing I felt and saw a spaceship move swiftly through the village and people were looking up at it. I heard a strange sound, like a bat or a bird going over my head, as I dreamed then I woke up.

The woman came closer and closer to me. She had a very light complexion. She embraced me; she also played a small horn that looked like a trumpet. Also, she played a soprano sax. She talked to me a lot, even though there were other people there at the occasion. She liked me very much.

I looked in a bag and saw the buds of a big marijuana plant. There was another man; a cleaning lady was going to clean the room. Some dirt was on the floor, so I swept it away. I thought it was the marijuana at first.

I was at a large mansion. Of course, I was very tranquil and patient. The beautiful blond woman liked me very much. I watched her, as she attended to the children, and I remembered walking with my hands in my pockets. Then all of a sudden, she called me and said, "Come." She had great affection for me. I wanted to be with her, but it seemed that she was mine forever, so there was no rush.

The one on the motorcycle took me where I had to go. He was very much fun, and then I remembered that he had done the same before. When I ran into the little girl, she questioned me like before. Everything was a repeat.

I went back to the beautiful cream mansion, and it seemed that I was throwing a big party. Everyone was already there, and I was thinking that I should have asked her to throw the party, but the party was very successful, and she was very happy.

I looked at her; she came over as she looked at me.

I saved the little girl.

I was trying to get everything extended for school by my male professor.

She gave me a tender French kiss with a surprise.

The pages of a certain chapter of the Analects of Confucius were missing from my brother's library.

My sister cooked a wonderful pork chop steak, which I ate with surprise.

The woman of creamy hypnotic slow movements kissed me tenderly; her warmth was like an oven. I was cool and cold, as I held her in my arms.

Someone had tried to frame me, but the key people let me know who it was.

We ran and hid from a tiger of great size. The tiger attacked and ate. It even attacked another tiger.

I went to a lecture, and there was a man that I knew there; he seemed to be disappointed with me but nevertheless respected me. I also knew the lecture.

The reality of two warriors uniting the world with brotherhood and love. Warriors had the same dream of meeting in a mystical world full of love, no violence, a world where they learned to feel and be creative with their mind and emotion. The beautiful black goddess taught them the art of love. Conflict in battle was where they become friends. At their high level of skill, they decided to escape the battlefield. By underground, they traveled to a new place of wonder and enchantment.

I put some important items in my locker. Then I opened up my locker again to see if the combination on the lock worked, and it did. My padlock had red on it, then I was on a level with another person that if we made the wrong move, we would fall, so he and I gently moved away. We both slid down a board that looked like an ironing board. Mine wouldn't quite come off my back, but finally, it did. There was someone watching me to make sure it came off. As I looked through the window, I noticed there was a woman trying to get me to listen to her say something, but I couldn't hear her. I only saw her lips moving and her hands moving. So she came into the bank and introduced herself to me. I put out my hand to touch her, and she responded by showing me her rectangular name tag on her shirt. I showed her mine and told her about the essence of having a friend. As we walked up the bank's stairs, she finally grabbed my hand because I said I would come to her wedding. I could feel the warmth of her hand. On a scale from 1 to 10, I rated her appearance as an ordinary 3, and she was very large and heavy. Then I said good bye to her, only to see more little friends.

The lady wouldn't let the person have the meat, so I told her I used to work back there, and they were going to throw it away anyway. I told her have a little heart and she did; she agreed with me. I was having a great time when I realized I was supposed to have a kindergarten class with Ms. Freeman. There was a man who was calling me with curse words. I told him that the ancestors would get him if he kept on doing that. When I got to my class, he was ready to give me new instruments for my students. I was in a store where a lady prepared a Japanese exhibit and another lady prepared a Christmas exhibit; they both were very colorful and bright.

The captain of the ship jumped overboard into the water, then someone took off with the ship; it began to move, then I felt it fly.

The monk was dressed in classic clothes. He called to the lion to taste the butterfly because someone was pregnant. The lion gently tasted the butterfly with its tongue. Then as the monk and the lion started to walk away and take their journey through the rough terrain, the monk accidentally stepped on a long live snake. The monk stepped on a heavy stone and rolled it over the snake's long body with one of his feet. The snake went into a hole in the ground, screaming with pain all the way in, until there was no more snake above the ground. Sand from the ground automatically filled the hole up; the monk kept his foot over the hole to project his chi or energy into the hole the whole time the sand was filling the hole.

A very close woman gave me warm contact.

I prayed with a Saint Thomas monk.

I traveled to other dimensions with two guides. I saw a bakery and tasted their bread. I met a woman friend.

My father showed me how to plant and also discussed the planting of various vegetables.

I was with a group of people, traveling to a particular place, a house. I had to use the bathroom in the bottom of the house of the basement; there was a square opening in the floor. When I opened it up, I saw large amounts of human waste, so I didn't use it. As I was opening it, there was a small black animal that I picked up and rubbed. He felt good, so good that I wanted to continue to rub him. He also had a unique type of voice.

As I read and went deeper in the ocean, she knew my desires; she was reading like a newspaper.

I was high in secret dwellings, looking down on other areas.

I went down long corridors, with several doors and toilets, until I came outside. There was snow, and I could breathe better. A person asked me, "Was that better?' and I said yes. Before that, I was in a room with some people, and then I started to sweep the floor.

Their heads looked like spaceships, but they had bodies like humans. They flew at fast speeds.

I asked them where the Martians were and they said they were here.

I met a famous woodcarver sculptor and shook his hand. We talked to him about art. I also had a special seat and two people were jealous, but God told them to do well and their reward would be good. We were up in a beautiful mansion in a celestial realm.

I was with some type of fraternity that had to do with everything high. Their boss was in or outside the dwelling. We and another friend were caught inside and the window to avoid our leader. We ran like a locomotive train at high speed. A group of the runners fell. But the first runner of the pack was the friend who was almost caught in the house with me. Everyone got a football and bowled to the master. I was the last one to get a football and bowl.

Three strings of tears came from my eyes. I curled back into a place, as I caressed them with mysterious attention. There on an elevator was a large ancient school of the past. Familiar yet strange, hopefully, the elevator operator could give no significance to my lost key in the blue bag.

The merchant was very terrible looking and huge; it came after me. It was trying to bite me, but I crushed the merchant; it was made of glass.

The two deer came after me because I was approaching the school. The old man with them tried to give me a hard time. With bottles and broken glass again but I escaped his plan. I was wearing a cute small black hat that the three ladies couldn't ignore; they talked to me but went with someone.

My mother cooked various goodies: biscuits, apple pies, etc. I woke up and saw my father and brother sleeping. I immediately took the phone and placed it in a calm place so that it would not wake them up. I ate some of the goodies after my mother had left.

I was walking in a place where someone was very mad; he was driving a car, but when I saw him, he calmed down.

DREAM 1

I WENT TO A FAMILIAR apartment building site. The first time, no one was there and the site was open; the second time, I sensed that the Rastas were living there. Clothes were hanging out of the windows, and I couldn't get in. I sensed that the complex was locked down. I found myself getting a ride in a car with some strangers. I noticed that some liked me and some didn't, but there was one of the strangers that played an unusual instrument, and he looked like a clown. The tune and rhyme that he played by blowing air with his mouth into the strange instrument made me concentrate my humming and singing abilities along with his into a funky beat of lyrics in sound. I found myself with no clothes on and was becoming significantly aroused as the stranger put his hand on my back. Another stranger tried to put his hand on my arm, but I took it quickly off because the sexual feeling intensified, then I woke up out of the dream.

I signed in, but Mrs. Ashley was sleep. I went to two meeting for the teachers; at some time in the last one, I saw Mrs. Robles, and she said that I signed in on the back of someone else's keypad. She was very disagreeable. They took all the food away before I got to eat. My brother Leslie said something to the fact that he would check me later.

I went into some lady's house and was looking for something when she came in. She knew it was me. I pulled the curtain back and saw her; she was very dark and large. She really liked me a lot. I could feel it, so we embraced. She was almost naked but told her that I would come see her on the weekend; she agreed.

I went to eat breakfast at a lady's house, but I told her that I would put a shirt on and come back there. People were already at her house ready to eat.

The car that was ahead of me crashed. The lady in the car crash had a baby with her; she asked me to take it to a certain place that I had just come from earlier in the dream. I didn't have a ride, so I got a ride from a truck driver. I hid the baby in a bunch of clothes that I had in a type of suitcase that was very small and slim, but when I was riding with the truck driver, the baby came

---

out of the suitcase as a flower; the truck driver saw it and fainted. Some other men breathed on it, and it faded in energy.

I was somewhere getting a bus. There was this fellow who seemed to make me stop in my tracks. I dropped some coins and I could see them very clearly. The price had gone up, a dollar and a quarter, the man said. The bus driver said that the kids are getting rougher. I knew that they just wanted more money. As he was driving, I jumped off the bus. The bus driver turned the bus over, an accident, more or less; I got my finger cut a little. But I noticed the others on the bus had some minor and major injuries. One person had a cut across the eye, another had a bandage wrapped all across her face. I noticed that as I looked at my cut, there was nothing inside my hand; it seemed to be a machine or mechanical. As I was walking, I looked into a window and saw a man painted white in the face, wearing all white clothes. He seemed to be a medicine or magic man. There were musical apparatus of every nature in the place where he was. It seemed as though someone was dancing or he was dancing. He seemed very calm. I waved to him, and he waved back. As I looked at him, I got a feeling of mystic India. He seemed to be doing some type of ceremony.

As I danced in the situation, I waited for an opening. Then I saw a lady talking on the phone. I waited by a baby crib; the baby was a beautiful brown color. I matched my color with the baby and waited.

The green animals bit deeply into my astral flesh, leaving long thin wires that I would pull out. After they were out, a green substance would come out of the holes. The animal's bite was very painful; I had to pull them off my flesh.

I was singing songs and playing on an instrument that looked like a comb. My brothers accompanied me for some reason on one song that was a romantic song to a woman.

I was in an area that was similar to the island, but we, my big brother and I, were in a car. Next to me in the car was a being that resembled an islander of native origin but was like a monkey in his body curves, but he was intelligent. We asked him to take us to his house; he was skeptical at first about us. Then after I told him about my brothers and how he was English too, he let us go to his house. He put his arms around me, as we sat in his house. I could feel that his body was similar but different, more curved and short.

I was in a locker room, putting everything in place, but I had certain keys.

CALVIN EARL DALLAS

I dreamed of a big black German shepherd being my friend and a little girl being with me. She said that she was from Dominique. Also she said that she wasn't a little girl and that she wanted to go back to Dominique.

Some bicycle guy almost ran me down, but he didn't hit me.

I was in a place in an apartment. I was talking Spanish to a light-skinned gentleman. In one room were three beds. The sun or light was just right. In another room, there was one bed. It was nice; the door to this room wasn't complete. My brother was there. There was a party, and this lady who had a lovely voice was singing. I told her that she sung beautifully. There were some other ladies there that were very jealous of her.

There was a swimming pool and the water was clear, so I got in and started to swim with part of my clothes off.

I was getting a new wave haircut, but the man did it without my approval. I was in a huge learning center. When he was finished, he said I should keep it pressed.

I was told to go to a certain place to eat breakfast, and the lady there was cooking eggs and cheese. I told her that I wanted tomatoes, onions, and peppers in mine. It seemed to me that I ate this meal very fast.

I could see that the first baseball batter was cursed by everyone, but the moment I went up to bat, it was very quiet. I felt what the bat felt like. I could feel the one I wanted to use. I felt the balls, and I felt the one I wanted to use. But when I was ready to hit the ball, there were too many people from the audience in the way.

I was somewhere in a building, walking down some stairs; a man was taking some pictures of me.

She was the rat I tried to kill but couldn't, then it turned into a woman. She defied me, looking into my face. She didn't touch me but warned me. I had to respect the rat woman.

It seemed as though my subconscious mind was doing the picking of subjects. I had a very fast car that I was driving. I ran on water. I could move by using the power of my mind. Everything in the dream was so clear, but when it was time to go to another place, my brothers were trying to help me, but I had water or power to start my machine car.

I was at some gathering in an institution where sports were the main focus. There was a giant player who became my friend. I tried to avoid it, but it happened. We went to eat and found ourselves running the way. It was very unique.

I offered my brother a special shaving device.

As I ran, I floated from one step to another. I was in a graceful slow motion, extending myself in timeless space. I enjoyed my strategy with focus and concentration.

I was with Mr. Newton; he wanted to know how much the artwork was. I wondered why he wanted to buy it. Then he maneuvered around me quickly on his feet. There was another woman who went into the chocolate, and then Mr. Newton tried it. There was an image of a baseball glove when he tried it. When I tried it, there was nothing, but someone assured me they would get something together for me, a woman's voice.

I was in a dream practicing with a sword, a long black Boca sword. Swirling with the sword on the downward stroke, I came into a basic aikido stance. Than after doing this procedure several times, I tried to spar with one of the masters. He was very good, but his quick reactions and speed countered my every move. I could feel his every move. I could feel his energy every time I attacked him.

I had a dream that I was flying and trying to catch the current of the wind. But I flew without wind current, and I finally ran into a giant.

I dreamed I was putting hot water in the pool, letting everyone know that the pool was too hot.

I received some rice, pudding, and other cakes from Aunt Essie; everyone was in a hurry to leave.

The water came flowing fast to flood; when I punched a hole in the third mesh funnel, then I showed myself a strange machine that stop the water.

I remembered buying a ticket from a man from a vehicle. He gave me a maroon purse twice, and I was feeling good and laughing. I took a seat and noticed some black woman who didn't look happy or inspiring at all. There was a man smoking next to me.

We were outside the store, and the salesperson, a man, got mad at us. He started to close his door; I hoped that he wouldn't so that he could have enough air. I was with a group of people and a young lady; we were very calm and relaxed. It seemed as though I was the leader. I told everyone to leave or go because I knew he was calling the police. We all headed down the stairs; at one point, she asked me to wait, but I didn't want to hear her say that, so I kept on going and I told her that.

Dad let you go into the garage to get your stuff; he wanted to know what park the children went to. You told him Lincoln. He left the keys in the garage, but while in the garage he didn't see my things: shoes, jewelry, a silver watch, and necklaces.

Some people were traveling in a plane-like vehicle, then they came out of the vehicle, and as it was traveling went back in, they landed in a crack to go into a house that was under the earth.

DREAM 8

I WAS TAKEN TO A city with a woman, then I left her to meet back with her on my journey into the city. I saw and met exciting people. A church of people who looked very different, light skinned; they looked at me as well. Then I met another group of people who seemed to be doing experiments. I asked one of them for their contact numbers, and they asked me for mine. I asked him to drive me to meet my woman friend.

DREAM 1

THE FAMOUS MUSICIAN WAS there. I talked to him, and he was playing his music outside while I was inside the pyramid building something. I could hear the music very dimly; this made me feel close in. So I came out of the pyramid to hear him. I kept thinking that I wish I had brought my trumpet.

DREAM 7 AND 3/4

I WAS SWIMMING IN WATER getting white clothes that were somehow the river. I collected them in a safe place. I notice an underground dwelling, in under the water, where a teacher was teaching some children. I hid so that they wouldn't see me. They were practicing a song or some type of music. Then they took a break. I went up to the surface to where I lived in a colorful bright boat on top of the water.

DREAM MYRA

I WANTED TO SEE MYRA because I needed some socks. So I went upstairs and knocked on her door. I saw that she was on the phone; when she heard my knock, she told the person she was talking to that she had to get off the phone. When she came to me, she said that I should call her on the phone when I want to see her. I responded by saying to her that if she wanted a robot, it's not me, then I told her bye.

DREAM O

I TALKED TO ANOTHER BEING in detail about a spiritual experience that I had, where the spiritual fire filled me up. After that, we saw a baby elephant and wondered where the mother was. I took the being for a small trip in flying.

The being was on my back, and we managed to glide.

The movie projector showed two pictures at the same time, one for the teachers in one basement area and one for the children. I asked the coach if we were going to have a fast track team this year after I had stopped long pieces of steel and ore metal from falling on someone.

I have an abundance of spiritual, physical, beautiful, hot, sexy, gorgeous women who love me intimately as well as sexually.

I am the best tai chi master in the whole universe and in the whole earth.

My second mansion or castle is manifest and is here now, and I'm in it living right now as we speak and am living in this dream come true home of an estate. Thank you, Jesus.

I have millions of dollars right now and can invest and can donate. I can spend for leisure. I can travel. I can wine and dine beautiful, free, creative, and career-oriented women, and I am totally successful.

———m———

One black lady was being beaten up by a white lady. I saw this and went to help her and got to the white lady and started to jack her up or tell her off, and the black lady said to let her go. They threw a book on top of the church roof; as it fell off, I caught it. It seemed to be familiar. They didn't see or feel me. The church ladies were there. The Moslem brother came by again and said, "I knew you were the one." I said, "Thank you. I appreciate it." There was a man flying a plane; he found the women with a group of people at a certain house where there was snow. He sat with her and kissed her in the mouth.

The big semitruck was moving and didn't know how to stop it, so I went to get my brother. I drank a dark liquid that tasted smooth, and I shared it with two other people, a lady and a guy.

I slept with a beautiful lady I tried to make love with, but I couldn't stay hard; she really wanted me to keep going. There was another woman neighbor who cared for a boy next door a lot. The boy asked me to show him a technique, but I said maybe later. There was a man who called out my name and said greetings. There was water in her bedroom, and I tried to fix it up. My next door neighbor, maybe an old woman, wanted to sleep with me; she put a sheep over us at first. Her body looked thin, but then it turned a kind of brown, and her hair was long, thick, and black.

I woke up in a bed late. Dr. Scalar was there, asking my brother and a friend if they could get me to Pueblo (a grocery). I took a shower in a place where there were people looking at me, men and women.

Breathing techniques and eating rice helped dreaming. Also, a diamond ring and green stone are from a meteorite. I was in a race, but I couldn't pass anyone. There were a lot of runners running.

I played trumpet around people in a public place, just a little to get a feel, and met a person. When we talked and I told him my idea, I noticed that there were very large flying ants that were around us. We moved to a place far away down the hall; it was quiet, and the ants didn't seem to be there. I noticed the tai chi symbol on the ground. I told him I was into tai chi, meaning steel wrapped in cotton. I was trying to escape and found myself in a tunnel opening that had a lot of wires that were wrapped and protected. The cover had South America on it and a small picture of a person in that culture. As I looked down the opening I had come in, it was filling up with water. I wasn't going through it, but I wasn't afraid. I woke up. I felt trapped!

I was at an engagement where people were dressed up, and we were at a dinner party. I recognized some people I knew. But soon, I left the party.

I was at a place that was very beautiful, a lot of light, and my mother and other guests were there. Then I saw a beautiful black woman who said that the man with the cane was a double and the real man was dead. This was a staggering beauty called Barbara.

James got up early, shaved, and showered. I saw someone walking around in the shadows. That was my mom. Barbara came in with groceries; she said, "Help," in a rude way, and I told her don't try to ask me like that. I noticed that it was Gloria's faces.

I got ready to leave the party. I saw that there were yellow cabs, but then I went into the legislature meeting; they said I couldn't leave. Then a man's wife argues for me and left me. Let Akola came and gave me my glasses when I was about to leave the first party. Two Akola had beaten up some bullies; they called me to show me, and I told them that they are cool. I was excited, so I started to run. I was walking past some owners and their pit bulls. A loose black one followed me and fought all the other pit bulls and lost. He audibly attacks all of them. As he fought them, he changed from an adult to a puppy.

I was on a bus with long plan that took up a whole row of seats and wanted to roll them up, so to help someone have a seat, James helped me roll them up. I saw a light-skinned brother on the bus. He asked me if everything was all right. I said yeah and shook his hand and gave him daps. I was going to catch a plane with a group, but I lost them on the bus. I was at a dinner party with nothing but ladies of all kinds, and I was looking at them as they were looking at me. Then one came along that I really liked; she fixed my tie a certain way. Now all the ladies were attached to me, then she ran away and told my guide or guardian angel to find her. But I saw her run away. I ran into church to see what was going on but didn't like the vibe so I left. Iran in a city, then was in a rolling barrel that had some animal running under it. I saw Andrew went into the ladies' bathroom and men's bathroom that hadn't been used for a while. Two boys could not get themselves together in the race contest; they were supposed to be a team. One of the boys was very lazy. I saw them kiss a lady on her lip and then seemed to bite it. I noticed that her place was very close. I was travelling and wanted to talk to Andrew, so I asked my aunt if she had his phone number. I talked on the phone to phonate as I mixed herbs. She heard the sound and asked what I was doing and I said mixing herbs.

The little girl was to wash my back.

I was at university, resting on a balcony, and saw a lovely lady, who also had a room down a long hallway with no windows and was claustrophobic. I met my old cross-country coach, Mr. King; he seemed to be in the process of checking a test of tours, and I asked how he was and he asked how I was. I saw myself looking for a certain key. The university was different at this time.

One is a pole very high up. I painted the pole in stripes.

I was in meditation, high as a kite. James asked me to show him how to use the measurement. Lesley had smoke for someone who I said I would get smoke for forty bucks. He wanted Loraine to ask me what I was doing, and I asked her if the banks opened today and she said yes. One girl licked my feet in the dream.

I told two charging animals to get back.

I was in festive place where I saw Mom at party and said she wanted me to get married. I said, "You know if that were to happen, it would've happened by now." I washed all my colored pants. I talked on the phone and said to my cousin to think resilient while in the hood.

In a beautiful house, the rug that Janice gave me was torn from the floor, and I was trying to clean it with a shovel, and I hit a black dog who was very mad; he ran and hid. Next thing I knew, he was coming after me. I ran up some neighbors, and stayed in a neighbor's house; a woman was holding a baby and jumping for us to go through and wake up. The dog seemed to stand up and run in its two legs.

I was in a car with a man who had three kids. It was a fast racing car. He gave me a popsicle and another candy to hold while he drove. His children talked to him. Someone fired a man from working in a bar. I was in a place where a friend had a saxophone and I was helping another artist.

I was teaching a group of children than I had to go. Two other teachers took over the class. I lost my clothes then I invented one-piece clothing to keep me warm. I saw a piece of cloth with various stitches in it, but it had a long-beaded string running through vertically. I tried to get it out, but it was too much embedded into the cloth. It had a mysterious energy emitting off it.

My mother said I had a phone call. She wanted to know when I was coming for dinner. I asked her what she was cooking. I had made love to her previously in the dream. I told my brother Christopher off and asked him when he was going to grow up. All of them waited for me to go to the bathroom around the water and leave, but everything was natural.

The black dog was very physical and friendly; it wanted to be everywhere and it was, but someone fed it poison and it died in a car engine. My little Chinese friend choked me in the knee unexpectedly with a long, sharp, skinny object; he had no explanation. I cried to a beautiful lady friend who was working in like a drug-care center. She just ignored me. Leslie gave me a picture of his new girlfriend who disliked him being married to Gloria. The man was bitten by the snake once in the neck; the second time, the snake went for the man, he bit some from a tree that helped him become like the snake and confused the snake.

I dreamed that I was at a bar and had drunk too much. He was out in a hammock. The people were Spanish.

I saw my soul in the mirror, an out-of-body experience, and I looked at myself in the mirror but saw only a light in my eyes; it was very bright that it shocked me. Later on, I was in a place with my mother; she told me not to be afraid, and she looked at me and was shocked too but said nothing about the light. She told me did I want to have grits with her for dinner. I told her when I come home for the day. It's not easy to live in two dimensions at once. I played the game of money to win money in a nightclub with my bet of number 7. It came up all red, but they said

I didn't win a cent. A dog attacked me and wouldn't let go. The opponent kneed me in the groin, but I took him down to the ground in a leg lock.

I shared vibrant energy with the black lady in the morning and kissed her; she was very receptive.

There were gentlemen there who introduced themselves but did not get in my way.

Leslie's car became smaller and flew to the outside area from where it was in various parts, and her auntie's voice was telling me to hurrying up and retrieve it with the help of Leslie.

I was in place where many people were working on cooking. I remember being responsible for a large container of liquid. I wanted to lift it with a machine. There, a lonely passageway was clear, so I took it down this way.

It was in a large city, but I had to go down the passageway where everyone had stopped working. I woke up, and there was a person who told me to go down the passageway. It was raining a lot; I tried to leave where I was. I noticed that the water was very deep. One of the kindergarten teachers came to where I was, and I asked her about the conditions. Her feet were dry; she said it was fine. I whispered something to her and left; when I came back, there was a man at the door, one was sleeping, one took my hand and walked with me. He wanted a fight, but I didn't. From outside, Dallas and the locust house were all close up. Chris and some of his friends were playing some game in the back. I went to him and he said I had to eat at the picnic table because that's what Mom said. I thought about going to the park to eat. Then someone rang the doorbell, so we hid ourselves and went in the alley, but now, it had shrubs. I spoke through them to the form of the house. Someone in the front saw me; it was a girl or pretty young lady. She came back to the alley and questioned me about where I live. I told her I lived back here, but she knew I was from the Dallas family.

I sang a song with a group of kids.

I knew this girl from fashion and told her that I could get her in to see Barbara. Then another beautiful lady with a lot of kids showed up and was listening to what I was saying.

I hoped very much and levitated to the ceiling.

I felt uncomfortable and wanted her to go, and she finally died. The house looked in great shape but was totally locked down. No one in the isle seemed to be around outside; before this, I went into a store and bought food with strange money similar to sign notes. While waiting for the store to put my food in a bag, I saw myself in a mirror: light skinned, handsome, black, and very young.

I saw a beautiful white woman, who was a very good friend. She was tall and had brown hair; we were at a festival event. In her house, she had a picture of my face painted on the wall. The picture was in color; as I looked closely, I could see some of my hair was turning white. It seemed as though I had lived with this lady before. I wanted to embrace her, but the urge went away, and I held her hand; it seemed that only this intimate gesture was available. I talked to her graciously. I told a friend after giving him some vitamins to go to McDonald's and get something to eat. Of course when he came back, he had meat. I told him that I was a vegetarian. He said he was going back; at that moment, I thought that she should cook for me, but it didn't seem like that was taking place. I had an emotion of despair or slight hurt that nobody cared, then he said he would go back to McDonald's. I said never mind; he insisted.

One lady wanted me, so she grabbed my genital area, and I also helped a lady levitate.

I saw my mother; I told her that she was looking good. She was happy to see me.

A prominent figure of a man broke metal.

All her items were there, but she was mad.

I was in a church crying.

There was a doll of a female skeleton. Children looked in a window that had a key to the door to try and find the manager's apartment but couldn't. The fear of being locked in; the key had a pointy side and flat side.

Mother was in a place where she was more beautiful than ever, and Barbara took me to her, a kind of home complex; she spoke to me as I got close to her. Then I saw some dignitary woman give me a handshake; she seemed to be made of metal. She wanted my address; I tried to write it on black paper with black ink.

I was with a pretty young white lady in a neighborhood in Milwaukee. I told her that I had a dream about my mom, but that she had passed away. This happened in a store; there was another man there. Then we looked at a basketball court where people were playing basketball. I felt ashamed to take her there because she was white, so we took a walk down the street. Some tall and skinny lady commented, "Look at what I'm after now," and laughed. I said she was crazy.

I visited my father in his house. He was with a lady; she was interested in money. I saw three little puppies that I helped him clean.

I went around the city with three guys who were in the martial arts. We talked about internal and external arts. I lost my way in the city where my father lived and couldn't find my way back.

I went to a medical place to use the phone to call my father; a little girl wanted to sit in my chair, so I let her. I played on an old mouthpiece that some gentleman gave to me, but I couldn't get a sound. A girl or lady was there; she said he would take it back and make a new one. The horn looked very ancient.

I was with some old Indian women, and one sat on my lap.

I visited Carla; she was healing and didn't want me to hug her too much, but she was very fat. She wanted to go to the art center with a friend, so she left a vehicle for me to drive. I drove the vehicle through town looking at the people and the scenery.

I was in someone's room. I escaped out the window, and someone thought I had stolen something of theirs.

I traveled and saw a map of a foreign country.

I was in a room but couldn't get out. Below the room was the exit, but the room was filling up with some type of substance and there were people at first down there at the bottom of the rope.

I took needles out of one man's face.

I created monsters by the water.

She is beautiful, also young looking; her smile is radiant, and she helps me here, honey. Her energy is vibrant.

I'm creating my dream. Mom said, "Ask your father's permission," then there was the image of the sword, the power to create your own dream.

Mrs. Brown wanted me to sit next to her for dinner with my lady and the children.

Sam asked me to check on his paycheck.

The band was playing.

Spiraling hand and body movements by me and others, my instructor knew I passed the test. The others didn't. He didn't listen or do spiral movements; he wanted to listen to music while he took the test. The instructor talked to him hard.

They can't overtake you at both ends. Too lose for the neck, he had a long rope with someone, a man.

He tried to come into my house without me saying he could. I told him I would call 911 if he didn't go; he tried to push me with his arm. I went downstairs and told my mother. She listened to me, and when we reached up there, it was a different man there.

I was dancing to a pattern of jumping and stepping with a group in the street.

I was in church. Leslie and his girls were there. I started to feel sad for Mom. There were other people there too.

I saved a person from getting hurt on the elevator; we were trying to get to a certain area in this huge coliseum temple church. One man let us pass through a certain area; we got on the elevator several times.

I was in a shopping area where there was a great bakery. A lady was getting her hair cut, then I was getting my hair cut. I could see that my hair was golden and wavy, curly and smooth; next to me, there was a man with a piece of bread on his shoulder. I went to look for the same type; it was looking good, so I saw that only a few bread were left. We went into a room for ice cream, but no one was selling it. There were two men in there; one said hi to me.

I saw a big white snake in a room; I saw children and adults who were part reptilian with long tongues but white in race.

I was in a place with beautiful women who could change shape or seemed to be elongated. She peed on herself and then asked me for water. We were together for a night out. I told her not to eat right in front of my eyes, and she was riding a workout bicycle that would change her from fat to skinny. One time, she was so fat that I changed her with the water thrown on the floor back to skinny. I had power to change this lady. I even changed myself into some type of decoration when the name Paul was called.

I visited Dad in a dream and made his bed for him, but he slept with my brother James in the other room.

The famous martial artist and I used some type of machine in the dream to strengthen the hand. He said he was going to cook a meal for me but got high off some substance and gave the rest to me.

The only father I have ever had. My mother looked at me and smiled. I wanted to help my father.

The element of time was broken down in visual patterns in a dream.

Every student had to take with them a black case to the exam; everyone was called to ride in the black limousines. My friend and his girl were in one with me; he sat in my lap. I took him off me and sat him by his girlfriend. He took my glass and poured dark chocolate substance all over them. I asked him, "Is this how you get your kicks? I wouldn't have done this to you." He looked ashamed.

I was in Russia and had a white man for a guide, studying botany or biology; I visited a family and sat by an old lady on the sofa and talked with the guide extensively. I talked about doing better on the examination.

I was running from someone, and they finally caught me; they were tied up in a cluster bundle, and I showed them a card with my protector Jesus on it. A young girl was on stage, and I was acting out a part; it seemed as though I didn't see my director. She was talking to me and giving me points. I walked around in Russia, but it was very boring; there seemed to be nothing to do.

The lady hurt her hand while using a machine that helped her dig up the earth in her inside and outside place.

I was in her car; the motor was still running when this happened, so I turned it off and came out with the key. A friend of hers came up; his arm seemed to be bending in the wrong direction. We went to her place to see if she was all right. I told her I could have done it if she asked me. I would have tried the machine, and it seemed to be wild and wacky. Other friends of hers were there too. There also was my brother there; it seemed to be great peace for everyone who was there. We left and went to another woman's place; my other brother was there. She talked to us intensely. As she talked, I touched her knee; eventually, her boyfriend got mad, and we had to leave. She walked us down to the place where we exited. You could see the street with the cars.

There were many ancient ones sleeping in my mother's house. I went there to wash my dark clothes and saw my brother.

There was a woman rubbing my hair softly, and I turned around and looked at her; she was brown skinned, conservative looking, and had quite a pug nose. I asked her, "Is that all you are going to do? She said, "Just wait. The stick is going to break your back."

The cat wouldn't leave the room, so I tried to make him go with a broom, but he attacked me and bit my big toe. After that, I closed the door and he finally left.

My two brothers seemed to be waiting for the musicians to get themselves together, so we left and were going home. I played like I had four hands, while my brother stood behind me, and we waved at the little baby in the carriage.

Two millionaires stole my pastries and goodies. I was trying to do something else, and I had to leave. I left them in a place in the restaurant; a person who worked there said the two millionaires took them, except for the book of changes. I called someone on the phone to locate these chaps; one woman I told the reason why I had to find them. There was someone trying to get in my way.

I was telling a man who represented me as a manager or producer that I am the best filmmaker, in the world. I told him he was going to see, as walked in suits through the green park. I felt very intense, and in my mind, I thought of other great filmmakers who were like me. I kept seeing all the concepts shimmering down to one simple truth or point that seemed to be the honest essence of all formulations and possibilities in infinity, a staggering impact to my mind.

He attacked with the poisonous kiss; now the other man tried to use his knife but found he was paralyzed by the kiss. The attacker covered him. But just as he did, he felt the presence of something looming over. As the attacker looked up, he saw a very strange large colorful shape pulsating high over his head; the shape came down and engulfed the attacker and the man.

I was talking to a beautiful black woman, and I told her she was African; it seemed as though I knew her from before. She gave me some perfumed candies to taste; they were sweet and flavored, and I let her know by hand sign that I liked them. She smiled. Then another beautiful young pretty lady appeared; at first, I thought she was her daughter, but she was her friend. It seemed that I knew her too. All this took place at a sensei martial arts dojo. I knew him and his students; he seemed to be telling his students something important.

It was very dry; the water flooded the city. We were told not to swim in it, but the ground needed the water. The inhabitants in the city tried to take shelter.

I ordered two soups for myself and something for another person. One lady said that I promised her a deal.

I was in a home with my mother, and someone came to the door. I asked who was there because the window was black. The person was an oriental man, who was my friend. He had a gift for me. I could see it, new library shelves, but I thought I had library shelves already. My friend and I put them up in the house. He also put his name on the two columns, Chen. Then we were in a room where he used a water hose where water was coming out.

I was watching TV in a dark place and called to my father. I thought I saw someone in the room, then a man came at me. I flipped him hard, and then when he got up, he said he took care of the cracker. Then I saw a man talking to a little boy, telling him it will be all right.

I was in a large open garage, then I saw my sister, Sally, outside getting ready for some type of festival. Also, I was in some type of school setting.

I was helping a young person learn to use their mind faster, then a police came and I left. The city was quiet. I saw some familiar neighborhoods but didn't want to go into those areas because of dogs. I noticed that the vegetation was very green.

She came to my school in high heels. I kissed her and talked to her, and she was and is a lady of mine.

I was talking to a member and letting him know that I knew I was a dreamer even when I was a child.

I talked to a light-skinned lady who refused to listen to me but kept telling me that I am right.

My mother said I had to get out more. We talked about girlfriends that had been there for me.

She said I had to get about more.

I went to a party and saw my woman there. Another woman wanted my attention, but I was just happy to see the main lady.

The lady was actually with another man, but she was kissing me. I didn't want to continue.

There was a large secret powerful gentleman who seemed to know me and treated me with the upmost respect. He signed the check I had. All the ladies in the bank had a very disrespectful attitude toward me, cashing my check. The gentleman made it clear to them that he was the authority and he had the last say; also, he assured me that I had his highest respect.

I had a cane, very smooth, brown, and orange. I asked the professor would he like to try it; he did. He gave it back to me. But I met him in the car; he left the gathering, where I had met him. Someone shot it out of the house from upstairs, and it stuck into the ground.

I wanted to help the sister with the project. I was very close to her.

I went to the party on the great sailboat. But when I saw myself, I had a huge afro and sweatshirt on. I looked like a thug. I thought, *How could this be?* I went to the bathroom and looked outside; I saw all kinds of people. People and children passed me by; they didn't notice me. One of them was a little girl, who stood next to me closely, and I could even feel her energy.

I was in a different town. I went out to see the ladies in the night but was initiated into a word called Yeah, so I kept saying this word.

The little person would not get out of my mother's house; he just went into her house without any permission, I told him to get out, but he would just stay there. I tried to get him out, but he was like a heavy rock; he just didn't move. It was very difficult for me to get him to move.

I was in a place, sort like a college, there were police everywhere.

I met a wonderful lady, who was a threat to others, but it was overwhelming to see her. She was lovely and charming. I felt kind of dizzy and a little afraid.

I chopped off the head of a wooden man, who was part of an initiation.

I was in a natural setting, where rocks and trees were very large; some were cut down by us. We ran between these trees, and some type of insects bit us. The pain was so great. I could feel the pain of these insects somehow on our bodies, but we had to withstand the bites and pain and not go down.

The lady was going to give a lecture. Another friend and I were at the college; we talked to her about the content of her lecture. We have the pre-notes on her lecture. She is a lovely young white woman. I remember a black lady telling me to eat a mango; she threw the mango a long distance to me, and I caught the mango with one hand by my head without looking. Outside, people cheered as I ate the fruit of the mango; it didn't have much of the taste, but it had a unique design carved on it. Stripes all over it, I was wondering how it could have been grown like that?

The lady stole two hundred dollars from me in the computerized numbers. She took the paper that I had put down in the basket. I told the authorities, and they found her and the paper; the men explained everything would be okay. Then I played some type of sport game with the man. Then I was going to leave. I said goodbye to another group of men who seemed to be on my same level. I felt intense emotion but didn't cry. My man friend walked with me. I asked him should we look back; he said no.

The light-skinned lady had her leg over my shoulder, and it felt good. We rode together on the bus with a group of people. We came to a crossroad. I directed the road to the bus to take the left; at the end of the road was a large doorway. I called out to see if someone was there after I had got off the bus. A lady came to the door in a few minutes and answered, and then she went back inside. I could see across the street; a man got into a car and started driving in our direction. When the car drove up in front of our bus, it was blocking it from going any farther. The man inside the car got out; he resembled some type of police official. Everyone was quiet. He had some type of scroll in his hands. He rolled it out, and the guide or the lady coordinator who was with us was pleased to see the scroll. Then we all went inside the large doorway. I saw different metallic symbols and jewelry on the floor, so I picked them up. At that moment, the light-skinned lady said thank you. I gave those jewelries to her and told her that I found them on the ground. She repeated what I said. Then I went to find a quiet spot to relax away from everyone. The next thing I knew, there was another lady who wanted to join me. Then out of nowhere, a gentleman in a suit and tie who knew me said, "So I see you want to be with Calvin."

The lady said yes. The gentleman directed to a place on the other side of the wall where we were at. There was a medium-size collection of blue science books; he suggested that I use them. I asked him if I could have them all. He said, "Just take one. I know you that you like the cosmos."

But I couldn't see the details clearly enough or see the completed words or letters on the books. Then I got a call on my cell phone that was about changing the numbers on a new feature on my cell phone. I asked the lady did she have this new feature also. The lady said yes.

I had to stop a giant bus on the road. I was attacked by a man with a gun, and I took the gun and shot him with a red liquid. I told him he should have babies, and then we used all the water when we came to get some. He was a friend; he wanted me to stay at his house, but I wanted to take the bus home.

I was in another world where my guide took me to many places. One of those places I was supposed to meet him there; they said he had been dead and that I could come in and take a seat. I went in a museum to look at the women.

I had a house that kept being uprooted. It was made of wood, fitted on iron rods; one day, it was uprooted by an invisible force. A group of brothers walked by, they insisted that I let them help me put it back into place. They put it back, but one of them suggested that I anchor it down with four metal stars.

I gave a beating to a large pig with a skinny chair, hoping that it wouldn't come toward my house.

I walked with a lovely lady in a beautiful garden with lovely flowers. She wanted to fly over a barrier, but as we picked up momentum, I doubted that we would make it. We stopped and walked to her home. It seemed that we stimulated each other without making love physically. I could feel her presence even after I woke up.

—◊◊◊—

The party had a lot of people, and I had drinks with a white woman. She kissed me, and we became friends. I left her and went to another part of the city where I found myself climbing up a ladder with clothes and camera dropping out of my hands to the ground. I climbed down the ladder to retrieve these items, and out of the darkness, a black woman came with a long handgun in her hand. She pointed the gun at me. I said, "You better not shoot me or I will tell your mama," then in an instance, I took the gun away from her.

I was in a car riding with another man; we were going to some place, and there was a man driving us. It seemed as though we were dreaming together. I know that we had both went asleep in our separate apartments; the other man had been feeling very sick. I went to check on him, and he was in his messy apartment. I went back to my apartment; the next thing I know, I was in a car with him, riding somewhere to a place where it seemed like they have recruits for some type of secret service. I told the other men in the car, "Let's escape right now."

He is not willing to for some reason. I asked him if he remembered getting into this car or coming down the stairs to get into this car. Then I told him that we were in a dream. I saw these young people that they were recruiting and the place seemed familiar. The next thing I know, I woke up in a nice apartment room. I went to the next apartment room, and I saw my mother get out of bed. She was very young and pretty; she seemed to be in a hurry to get somewhere. I noticed when I went back to my room, things seemed to be sliding on the floor themselves, like the floor is slanted. I looked at the apartment and I saw that there was a little dog on the floor, a black-and-white Chihuahua.

We were taking an examination at a very good college, then we took a break and traveled around the city, but when we tried to get back, it was very difficult. The person I was with was also a student who took the exam; we asked the people in the city how to get back, and at one point, I knew how to get back, but the other student who was driving didn't follow my instructions all the way to the details, so he was driving down the wrong street. We didn't go down the main street, so he finally went over a wall purposely. Then we tried to walk the rest of the way. He said, "Don't worry about the car."

We asked people along the way; they seemed to be British, and they gave us detailed directions, as to how to get there. This college had many green fields where people played different sports and games.

I read a newspaper; it was in a celebration in a town that I knew very well. An older gentleman told me that his birthday was coming soon and that I should give him the newspaper. I said that it was mine. Playing catch with a football team of teenage boys in slow motion, like I was floating, was so peaceful and quiet.

I was in a place where there was an ocean, and I had purchased perfume, cereal, and other items. I got off the bus as it went into the terminal. Now I realized I had missed my stop. I had left certain items on the bus, but they had locked down that part of the bus station, where the bus had gone into. So I asked another bus driver, a brother, where could I go to get my items. He directed me to a window office, where a beautiful lady worked. She offered me a lot of what she had shown me.

In a country landscape, a pretty woman and man were on a horse surrounded by horses on green mountains and hills. As they lifted themselves up on the horses' backs, the scene froze into a still picture. The cattle and cows on the cottage farm had the same expression on their face as the man on the horse. Then the pretty lady froze into a still photo, I colored the picture in with oil pastels. I was riding through the same green valley, and I heard a musical jam session. I wanted to play on the tune, "A Love Supreme" by John Coltrane because in my mind, I knew that would be the next song. But I was in a truck riding by the musicians and people in the jam session. Someone called out to me, but I realized that I didn't have my trumpet; I left it far away at home, from the village. The truck kept going by the jam session.

The surrounding changed constantly, as I changed beautiful geometrical pyramid tiles. I went through the same pyramid palace several times like a drum rhythm; each time, the palace was more beautiful. Never been there before, but each time, I became more beautiful.

I don't know how it happened, but I went back to a place where I had gone to school, not on this earth but on another planet or world. I was supposed to be babysitting, but something kept the baby and a young lady who was with me saw an orchestra with three bass players. Two upright with hands and one with a bow, I asked the young lady why the youth played by reading music; she said they don't have too. She shows me around the place, hugging me the whole time. I felt like I climaxed, but when I woke up, I hadn't. The young lady was thrilled with joy.

I was in the movie theater and the people were very rude. They were in there doing things to disturb the movie, which was on a movie screen one hundred times small as the theater or almost the size of a television set. They took my baritone horn to another room, and most of the people didn't like the film.

I woke up out of a dream in apartment similar to the one I lived in, but it connected to a woman's apartment; this woman went through my apartment. I sensed this and got out of my bed. I looked out the door to the hallway; I noticed that she did come through my door. I locked my door.

I was talking to a man, and I looked out and saw a glass wall door; a lady with two children knocked on it. I opened it, and the first thing she said is "Calvin, quit worrying."

With that, she seemed like an angel and she stared at me and asked if I will go shopping with her and have dinner. I said yes. I had a feeling of being wanted. Her little daughter held my hand and then we walked very fast down a revolving staircase. I noticed I can't keep up. I was telling the man he had the potential to do anything. Now I was going down the stairs by myself, so I asked another lady did she see a lady in red go out the door? She said no.

I saw something through the bed. I noticed it was a person, so I tore up the bed to get at the image of a person. The person was a white noble European. Also I tore up his papers and books, as they surrounded him. I took a walk out on the town and went into one place, a dark lonely street, and there was a protector there with a sword and shield. Then I went to a Mexican area and watched people.

The box which rattled had something in it. I gave him ten dollars. I wanted him to empty it for the other ten dollars. He did, and I took the box and left with the woman in the red.

I went to the project area but seemed to advance with electrical circuits and with modern futuristic cars.

I was around the crime crew; one assailant continued to attack me. I watched him closely, and I countered all his attacks. His last attack was with a weapon. I applied a technique. I countered his moves and took the weapon.

I said I wasn't ticklish, so the woman massaged me very gently, but I wondered why her husband didn't look at me.

I had a lot of hair, like a Rasta, and I was sitting on the bathroom toilet and another woman was sitting on a toilet; a wall fell out so you could see the people in the next room.

I saw the inside of a large boat. It had seats for many people. There was a man on the outside of the boat, showing me how use the wood for the boat together with nails.

I levitated and then made a lady levitate. I felt that it was a mental urge or feeling. Then I went to a bar where a guy I had previously known tried to charge me too much money.

I destroyed an unusual being, who was my teacher in another world, but he had birdlike claws for feet and wore a mask.

There was a hotel, and we checked in. The room was like a shower. You could take a shower, and then you would have tables with ladies and gentlemen like you, relaxing there awhile.

There was a lady who said she was going to help me, but then, she made the statement that she knew that I wanted to make love to her or she wanted to make love to me.

She left. I followed her down some stairs and into a crowd of people, and I said to her, I thought you were going to help me."

She definitely felt the intense emotion but still declined. Then I met a Rasta; one was talking, and I listened. I had some clay and nails in my hands, so did he; as he talked, I made some type of African sculpture. I was finally on my knees or sitting in front of the Rasta who was talking, but I was still making the sculpture. The other Rasta left. A lady from the restaurant brought the Rasta who was talking a particular plate of various dishes, but it wasn't food. Then I noticed that more rooms had been added on to the restaurant or hotel. I could see them, but they seemed to be empty, so I tried to get a room. Next thing I knew, I was in a room and a friend of mine introduced me to his mother who had passed away in real physical life.

She was getting a massage; there was a lady there who told me to put on lady shoes so that she could check and see how strong my legs were by touching them. But I took them off. I wondered why she wanted me to do that. I asked her if she usually did that to people. I can't remember what she said. I looked at my friend's mother; she was more beautiful than ever. My friend brought me some refreshment, orange juice, but I was thinking red wine.

I was looking at a very beautiful woman; she was very shy. She turned her head from me with a great smile, then I saw an older man. He questioned me on several subjects, especially on my running, but when I looked closely at his face, I saw a crawling insect go into his mouth. At that point, I told him I had to leave; as I went out in the city, I noticed he was still following me.

I was playing a very long horn, but I could only get one or two notes out of it. It had no keys. I played along with the people who sang the national anthem; after that, a man came to me and said he usually gave money to help other people so that he would give it to me. He gave me a whole handful of money. I took it and put it in my pocket, then I laughed because I felt so good and told a friend that I would buy him a drink, but I never did.

I was waiting for one lady to give me a ride home while the other I was talking to said she would give me a ride home, then I woke up.

—⟍⟍—

The young men were very excited and had their speakers on their music boxes. I was listening to the sound to balance the volume; they were so excited that they kept knocking over their component set down. I noticed that I was running in dark areas where houses and streets were.

After I had gone in unusual directions from the monumental university, it had many levels and many students. It seemed that I had been there before, but I had made the turn and went into unfamiliar places. I was running in a black silk outfit, similar to a ninja. But I saw a large black animal similar to a dog in shape, I ran to get away from it, but after a while, I realized it wasn't coming after me. I saw a white man in trouble, maybe lost or confused about something. Then I observed part day and part night all in one sitting at the same time. I wanted to seek out more light because it felt good.

I picked up all dead bodies that had been drowned by the water. Doctor saw me. I was jamming with clothes as the choir sung with great steps. As I flew in the air that had a lot of water in it, I saw my old neighborhood, with children and bicycles.

The being shot an arrow through my ear. I wondered why it was not bleeding; they wanted to do it again, but I told them they were crazy. Also I had spent a lot of money at a party, but when I left, I saw two people blowing trumpets, one was very muscular. I caught a cab. Buses are a vehicle for transportation on or back to body or earth.

I drew a car which I could not stop. Right away, my double told me to keep on trying to stop the car when it went straight through a stoplight, and the double helped me to the car which was very old-fashioned and black.

I was in one dimension trapped by attackers. I went into an upper level in transition area. I needed no money. I was given a key and also saw various key people.

Running on another planet across mountains and sandy beaches with people playing was great. I'm in a suit covering my whole body like an astronaut. People were laughing at me, but it seemed to know that I saw snakes for an instant. I woke up and had plenty of energy.

I sat on rocky mountain with someone, but I had the sensation of falling. I could see a lady on one side of mountain and books on another mountain that was facing me. I wondered with the weight of us both sitting on this particular mountain why we didn't fall.

I was in a black truck with my friend, Gregg. The inside of the truck was larger than the outside. It also had mirrors all on the interior; you see your image several times. He was going to bonsai club. I got on the two-wheel bicycle and made my way to another place; in this place were some women asking of me. After I answered them, I left and heard the chief playing the questions back on the recorder. Then some beautiful women came into my sight. I went to the bathroom and saw a stall. I went into one with reddish wood. I saw money in the stall or pocketbook, and as I urinated, a man took the pocketbook. I went after him. He asked me to take some money, and I told him I didn't want money. He said, "You don't want money, then the worst thing you could do is snitch."

JUNE 21 2009

WEDNESDAY

I WAS ON A MOTORBIKE travelling fast. A lady helped me start the bike every time it stopped but refused me; finally, I was trying to take my big brother somewhere on the bike. He fell asleep, and I tried to wake him up. The bike wouldn't start, so I carried him. I kissed him on the cheek, but he was fast asleep.

I was in the house that was very large, living by myself. Two people came to visit me; they wanted to talk about music. Did he like reggae or some other? They went to the attic when they were full of water and going crazy, then there was a spout of water and it came on. I tried to turn it off, but it kept flowing. Finally, it came off after I turned the valve off. Then two of my friends appeared, kung fu martial artists. One had a large white beard and the other light. Surprisingly, I knew the history of these men. They seemed to be happy to see me. A duck caused water to overflow in the various rooms of the house; I tried to grab it. Then there were large covers that came over the house to fly. I saw it so clearly from the outside. I knew that the kung fu man was responsible for this. A brake fell off of the semi air vehicle. I tried to find this brake and a scorpion stung me.

I was in a complex trying to get away from some type of adversary. There were people doing various jobs. We traveled throughout the complex, and I evaded him through a window.

She took the money but tried to play it off. He looked perfect in the dream,

The light-skinned tall woman kissed me gently and closely, and I could feel the children coming. So I left her and hid by some other houses; the children found me. We were playing ball together, then I wanted to see again, so the children and I went to the light-skinned tall lady. She didn't want me to be in bed with her and her daughter who liked me also, so I played with the children.

My aunt wanted me to put a white robe, but I said now I was a suit, then she said that was still your teaching.

I was kissed for a long time by a beautiful black woman who told me later to come up; as she walked away, she looked at me. She had lots but only had one piece of material around her. I looked for her later but couldn't find her. I was making love to a beautiful woman and two young girls were trying to see what was going on and told them to split. As I pulled the covers over me and my lover woman, I was in another room with Ellen. I tried to leave to get myself free.

We were on two different taxicabs. I yielded the number, and he yelled the number.

We were in jail or in hold, and they wouldn't let us go to the bathroom, but finally, they let us go, and he said, "Have respect for Dallas," and he showed us a gold chain.

I saw a weight-lifting man who knew me as a friend.

The sculpture pieces that I made were glazed and had pretty secondary and primary colors, mostly secondary. I put that next to the car in a box. When I came back, there were other boxes, but there were other boxes but my box with the sculpture pieces were gone. I could tell that they were inside the car or truck and went to the people's house and introduced myself as the art instructor at Gomez. They were playing with the time. I told them I had not that much time; a friendly, warm lady gave me the key, and her friendliness was great.

I was playing in a band, a bass bus. All the players were waiting for this lady singer who was too slow and this karate man to do a great kick but he busted his foot.

Attacked by a vicious dog and its growls, I put them apart, then my companion dog attacked the vicious dog, and it went on a fence up high, watching him. I was at a synagogue with several black men. I and another man had a lot of photos of women and took a quick look at his and mine, then he wanted me to look at his again, but I wanted to look at mine. There was a great sense of power between us. There were many cookies for refreshments and children playing. Then it began to rain a lot. I was running through various neighborhoods and they seemed to be familiar, but I came to one that I climbed up on the roof and saw a set of keys on the roof, a nice sharp automobile. The man came out with a gun and pointed it at me in a slanted way, then withdrew it. He invited me into his place. We went into the basement, but then I saw a soft sweet light-skinned arm push the door closed for a moment and was in an atmosphere of benevolence and realized there was a beautiful woman with him. He had two bedrooms in the basement and offered me them for the night in a kind gesture.

I was in some unique place that I was trying to get a job washing dishes. It was like a place of learning. Universal Mother, I need a great woman. I know that you're going to give me one soon.

In one of my dreams, I was speaking Spanish. A woman asked me something in Spanish. At first, I didn't understand, but after a while, I answered in Spanish. Another friend wanted to take me to another Spanish city in Puerto Rico.

My sister was scratched by a cat. No blood, just bright color. I tried to chase the cat away with a chair. Many competitors sat in sophisticated console. To relieve them as we did, these people observed us from the open. There was a man who asked if he could hear my tape. I said no, that it was personal.

The animal looked like a bat that was flying happily around. There were several; they didn't attack me and my oldest brother, but they were short and had short wings and very sharp teeth.

The two men, one white and one black, volleyed for my attention, but the black one seemed to be the godfather for me.

The photo captured moments superior in time out of time.

She was telling him something personal about their daughter, Maria, and I was in the bathroom and heard everything. I became emotional, almost crying. As I changed my shirt, he came into the bathroom, and then I eventually left as he was washing up or changing my clothes. Someone told me to lock the bathroom; whatever she told him was limited. I told him my knees were getting hard, and he said they're not supposed to.

There was a woman who spoke a foreign language. Another woman helped me to talk to her. She was pretty and went to the cafe to meet her, but most of the people I knew nothing of. In fact, some dishes fell and broke as I looked at them in the showcase.

They were waiting for me. My father was in very dusty clothes, and when he saw me, we shook hands.

They brought back a mixture from the moon; it was in a bottle but only a pencil could get it out.

I was naked and went to a place where people lived in a small compartment and elevators were in use. I think it was a university some called the mansion. Another ancient order. I was right next to this person. I think I knew him.

There was a TV in each room. Mother and Father showed pictures of vast mountains. I spent a lot of time with my father making a fireplace, then I spent time with my mother.

We were traveling, two men and a lady, looking for a place to get money. The lady had the credit. We stopped at the appropriate place and went inside; we waited for her when all of a sudden, the other man came out of somewhere with a flame of fire on a torch. He had it under control, then we we went out of the room, then the lady appeared happy to see me. We went out of the room; the man with the fire had turned it into a couple of drinks: three unusual with dark-brown color and white sugar on top. I took some of the sugar or white substance off mine.

I dreamed we were letting some birds fly away. Other people and I started when a woman took a picture and gave it to another woman; she balled the picture up. I was not too happy with the idea, so I pursued the lady to give me something in return for it. She gave me something, then I was in a place where filming of these beautiful birds was taking place. As we let them go free, some changed to beautiful fishes. I was with the crew, filming this, and I saw familiar faces asking me if I needed help. They seemed after a while to get in the way. It seemed that we were in an underground cavern or world that was part water and part sky. The next thing I know, I was in this very long and strange fast vehicle. I was in the front with someone. I was driving but yet after your whole thing was to stop the vehicle, but we couldn't. Finally, we did in. We were in the neighborhood of doom, so we stopped in another location not too far from that and someone brought a person out who was very much in pain or hurt.

I shook his hand; it was very light, almost folded with a crack, then the small creature was wooden. Descent kept coming until finally, I looked one right into the eye; it touched me in the arm with a pointed mouth. Its eyes were light green.

We met in the room; it turned into a boat in which I drove down the streets very fast with wheels. Finally, we wound up at the sea and said we couldn't take the boat out in the ocean because we didn't have the right papers.

The substance was very fulfilling. It was a vegetable unknown to me but quite tasty. My sister was very sensuous. The woman drove us in the cars but we seem to be overpacked.

We were exchanging gloves, and it was cold.

I was at two parties at once. I was really drunk, and at the other, I had control over myself, and I was in a church sitting, waiting for a choir to come in. A great choir people were expecting me to be represented.

I put out the fire in my house; my brother was asleep, and my sister told me about it. Then I found a shiny thing sticking me in the shirt. I couldn't find my key to the house and door.

There was a lot of wine in the temple; my father told me to take as much as I wanted. My older brother felt that it was wrong, but I did it anyway.

She balanced the foundation as I stood on it to get the paper; other teachers were there, Ms. Rhyme and some more.

I was on the bus, and women liked the way I looked. I had my Washington High sweater on.

The enemy was a fierce black or dark-colored dog. After doing some procedures in the class, Ms. McCoy climbed on my back; the dog came very close. I told someone to let me handle it. I did nothing physically, but spiritually, I felt I did something because my boss had goose pimples. The dog turned around and left us.

I told my mother or someone who looked like her that my sister was receiving a present. She looked at me and finally answered.

All the blue jeans were on the dresser, but Father packed them all into a large beautiful bag next to his bed or a bed next to the dresser. I felt that he was not going to let me have them, and I argued with him. He told me he had his ticket that showed he paid for them and said the same; he told me to be quiet and sit down so I did, but I still argued with him.

I talked to Kathy on the phone to let her know I still loved her and even went to her place to see her in person; she was pleased.

My oldest brother was supposed to take me out to a disco but never did.

I went to a house with a friend. There was a strange woman there whose vibes I didn't like, so I ignored her and went into the base; my socks were full of holes. There were many chambers and rooms with doors; we went through most of them until we came upon the coordinators for the children's program. My friend went to sing his song for them, so he did; it was very beautiful. I never play you off was part of it.

Father asked if I was all right. I said,

"Yes, and how are you?"

"Fine, but Eddie said we have not been treating him right, so he is going to leave. I saw him with his suitcase."

"Try to explain, Father."

The fat lady that I stood closely next to helped me make the green solution for the little girl.

I had a dream I took a young girl out of a box; she had plenty of insects with red marks inside of her. I could see them crawl out of her on the edge; she wanted to get them out and move her over so that she could get them out and ask her who I should marry and she said, "Doreen." I dressed up as an Arabian woman and had a beautiful outfit on. I could see the blue lines in the black. I had put makeup on my face. I told the girl with the insects inside of her to get down from being so high in the air because I didn't want them on me. I was trying to put her back in the box or package, but I noticed that she was real and her body parts were three-dimensional with these insects inside her body but no bones. There were quite a few in there. She said I should marry Doreen. I remember playing with the Arabian outfit with the scarf over my mouth and pretty shoes or sandals on my feet and the shirt-like dress on my lower portion. I saw that I had a little makeup on.

I saw a person punch a person several times and look like he had two weapons; the person who got punch closed their eyes.

I remember several people, women and men, dressed in black; it seemed as though I knew them.

I remember Leroy taking something from me and then I got it back. One person was a man I met who wanted my shirt because it had a lot of symbols on it, but I didn't want to give it to him.

I was in a cafeteria trying out various kinds of foods. I saw paperwork and places to sign. The city had pathways to go and live. The man said life would be better; he talked about a famous musician that I knew, so I shook hands with the guy. The angel came; I asked him what size of shoes he wore. Someone wanted to hug me, but I didn't want a hug.

As I was getting away from someone, I found many rooms to escape into.

My body became very hot and started to do various exercises, then all of sudden, beautiful black women appeared on my bed. I didn't know her. I started to hold her and kiss her, but I noticed she had no desire. Her skin seemed to be transparent and wet at some points.

I asked the author and his friend how they were doing as I stopped my run. His friend, who looked familiar, said we got everything taken care of, but said not one word after that. They seemed to discuss very quietly something, as I observed them. Then I opened the door and there was a new drum set and piano. I believed that Arthur had left them there; the other people in the house with me wanted to play the piano. It was of a usual nature.

As I talked to the girl, I felt that I knew her from childhood and that one side of her face had a little bit of skin, but she was kissing me a lot.

There was a lady who was poisonous and was coming toward me. I told another lady to keep her away, but she persisted and we fought; she was as strong as a man and had no sensitivity.

The furniture in the house was very strange and orthodox. Mr. and Mrs. P wanted to see me. I had a unique cane I walked with.

I was in a house, and all these people came and started moving in without asking. Finally, I told them who are they to do this? One man gave me his name and I told them to just be honest, that I was an American citizen, so they all packed up and left, but before that, I played with some type of musical device. After they left, all this took place outside in a parking lot, even though it started in my house.

As they drove away, I heard someone, a lady, call my name several times, "Calvin, Calvin, Calvin." I saw her get out of the car and come running to me; she hugged me and said she had heard about my sister Victoria. We had both cried, then she asked me how my sculpture was.

The lady was very heavyset. I was looking at her artwork. She had short white pants and a t-shirt on.

She seemed to be very beautiful and strange. She came out and seemed to be very intense and focused.

Something was bothering her; she said something to the fact that things were not going the way she wanted them to be. Then I said everything happens for a reason, and then she walked in front of me. It was a very sunny day, then she turned around to go back inside, and her hair seemed to change from the color brown to a bright white in a moment, then she continued to go inside. I was on the outside behind, observing her, then I saw a young boy dressed in white. I had a feeling that this was her son; she went to the boy to hold his hand, and then all of a sudden, they vanished through the outside wall of the building that her art was in. The wall seemed to have a faint circle painted on it; this is the place where they disappeared. There was no opening. I started to go through the circle, but I felt and sensed a hot vapor or a steam or gas that got intensely hotter as I tried to go forward through the wall,

Finally, the heat became unbearable to the point I had to turn away. A golden ball came out of the faint circle area. I felt it coming very fast to hit me. I was aware that I was now inside of a game. I had to hide behind various 3-D structures; as the ball went around at great speeds, it would crash into these3-D structures that I would hide behind for protection. The golden ball seemed to be circling in cycles of great speeds.

She had a lovely tattoo of flowers over her body, and she kissed me sensually, then we went to the beach. I thought of her boyfriend. One of the men on the beach said she was the best beauty he had ever seen. Someone offered me something to eat and asked me was I from here. I said no thanks.

I went to St. Croix with Holly and some other musicians; they looked like they had just got up. Holly played the drums and another person played the bass guitar. I left them and took a run. On the way back, I saw a cow being taken up from the ground; he seemed to be spread out more than normal. Two other people were getting him off the ground, but he was yelling. Then I saw other people in the house looking at me; when I walked by, they closed their door. All the lights in the city had been turned off. I was wondering how I would get back home from St. Croix because I had school tomorrow. Then I looked for Holly.

I was in an elevator with a friend and other people. The elevator stopped between levels; it seemed to be a weight problem, then a man in the elevator adjusted the weight with his own body. I told him thanks, but he said nothing to me. Then my friend and I went to his apartment where his wife or girlfriend was waiting for him. He had asked me to hold a gift for him and give it to him when we got there.

I was in a shop that sold bread and other dishes; for some reason, I ordered a lamb because they didn't have any boneless fish. The people behind the counter, the woman and man, spoke in a unique Spanish that I could understand. The man got a small frozen lamb and showed it to me, and then he started to cut it up. I didn't look, and when I did look, it looked like he had hollowed out a basketball type of watermelon fruit. He was drinking a red substance from a cup; all of a sudden, a lady came swiftly in the shop and burned my arm with a hot iron she was holding. The iron felt more sticky than hot, and then I woke up.

I needed the shovel to get the ice out of the living room. One of my brothers had been working on something outside, but when he was finished, he accidently threw the shovel in a dry well that was about twenty feet deep. I was trying to get his attention to go and get it, but he seemed too busy to notice me. I went to the garage looking for another shovel; when my mother came walking toward me, she said, "Don't you hear me calling you, boy?" She looked great. I wanted to kiss and hug her and comfort her with the touch of my hand; she gave me words of affection and an abundant smile. Then I saw my brother go over to the well, which had filled up with water right before my eyes, and he dived into the well, feet first to enter because it was not that wide. I tried to tell him not to go into the well because it was to narrow, but he jumped in anyway.

I helped a lady escape a very dangerous person. I said to his face that he could not take the lady; he tried to tell me that I had no right, but I continued to help this lady. We, the lady and I, got out of the building that the dangerous man stopped me in. We both jumped over a tall fence; first I jumped and then I had to inspire the lady to jump quickly over the fence, which she finally did. I gave her a little kiss on her cheek. Then I asked her if she had a car.

I was holding a little entity that had a white cloth over its body; it was making sounds that were very loud and ireful. On the other side of the room, there was a wall that divided the room in half; there was a light-skinned woman who held a crying baby. She let the baby get away and become one with the entity, who got away from me. The baby and the entity merged into a fire that was kind of flattened out by the white cloth that was over the entity's body. I tried to pick up the moving white cloth with fire underneath it; it was too hot. I tried to pick it up three times, and each time, the heat was unbearable. So the woman who had let the crying baby go told me to leave it alone.

I was in another world with my brother; we went from neighborhood to neighborhood, flying in the air with our own bodies. We stopped in and observed people's houses, groups of various functions and occasions. One of the houses I went to, I got trapped in; a beautiful black lady showed me a small wooden key that could open the door. After she put the key into the keyhole and turned the small wooden key in the door, and I opened the door and went out of the house. Then the door fell to the ground. I picked the door up and placed it back into its original position. It seemed to have no hinges or anything to secure or hold it in place. Two little boys tried to catch me while I was swinging on a rope; one showed me his little wooden cross on his neck. I said that it was good and gave him a handshake.

In one dream, I was washing my face, and a large woman bumped me out of way, as she passed in front of me, with her rear end.

I stopped a group of people who I had been practicing running with from coming into the house that my mother and auntie were in. I introduced my auntie to one of those people who I finally let in; my auntie felt so real, as I touched her shoulder.

I went into a store and got a package for health in the eyes; the owner said I didn't have enough money to purchase the package.

I was in a place where two beings, both female, seemed to adjust my imbalances by using a breathing technique, holding me close as one being, absorbing the imbalances in my hand and whole body; after that, I felt very light.

The man at the table showed several glowing and exotic gems in silver square cases, then he brought out a large slim rectangular piece of metal that was shining with gold and silver, and it had on it various hieroglyphics that glowed also.

I looked intensely at the beautiful young lady; she also looked hypnotically at me until I could see an invisible doorway keyhole superimposed over and between me and her face. She was sitting in a movie theater with her boyfriend; they seemed to have an argument. She sat in a seat away from him, and both of them sat not facing each other. I wanted her to come and sit next to me, but she didn't.

She got up and left the movie theater. I was still watching her. She was about to open a picture up on a pad of large drawing paper. She just lifted up one corner of the paper to reveal a very ancient and royal ancestral image.

There was a man who tried to overpower our mind; he said my neighbor was a coward and tried to get him to play a game with his large team. I told him I would call the police because I knew the law.

I was listening to some romantic music, and someone changed the music; a young man put some type of rock music on. He said my music was too sad. He put his arm around my shoulders and said he was fifty-eight years old; he asked me how old I was. I told him I was sixty-one years old. The young man said he was my friend. An older man was looking for me because he said I had done the breath thing with Marilyn Monroe on her album, which had her sexy picture on the cover. My friend and I, with two other men, went to the same house that I was in. I had trouble opening the door with the key, so we climbed in through the window in the back. As I sat in this house, there were plenty of people who had come to eat dinner.

I was sitting at the bar, drinking in a classy place. The bartender showed me red and white drinks in elegant bottles, I took the white even though I wanted the red. After a while, the bartender told me I had to spend at least a hundred dollars minimum. We argued and then he gave me my money again. He left and went somewhere and then came another set of bartenders, whom I told about my dealing with the first, but it seemed to me that he went looking for the police. So I left the bar. I had seen some familiar faces as I left, women who were housekeepers. I met up with a little boy in a neighborhood, who looked familiar. The young boy was very friendly; he talked too often and ran, played, and fell down often. We saw a place of books locked up and kept saying I needed the key to get the books, and we seemed to be going to a certain familiar area but never made it there.

The man wanted me to give him three dollars for three hundred dollar tickets, so I did give him the money. He took it humbly, but I noticed that they were very large, broken, and torn in some places.

I remembered seeing some type of being who looked like a rough 3-D mosaic candy assortment.

I was wrapped up in cloth, a certain type of brown cylindrical object. I felt I had done this before. There was a Rasta directing me, but he was speaking in island lingo. Then he left me alone.

I was in a conflict; people were trying to overcome me by tricking me to fall into traps. I used magical sayings to change the situation and escape those conflicting elements. The words gave me power to control my opponent. I lifted one person off his feet with my two hands.

I walked in a neighborhood with fine houses and then went inside one of those houses. I saw my neighbor preparing a lot of beautiful wooden chairs by attachment of decorative motifs on them; she offered me a bottle of wine. I was already drinking out of a glass and carrying some wine with me, but I still accepted her offer and took the wine. She laughed when I asked her a question.

I was driving the car through a city with a lot of traffic; the car wouldn't reverse. I was driving across the vertical traffic horizontally. As the traffic flowed downstream, I crossed the traffic midstream; the traffic seemed to slow down and wait until I corrected the direction of my vehicle. I saw police cars, big and small cars, trucks of all styles, not once did I get hit, and then my car started to slow down.

I was flying on a magic carpet, going very high and fast, then I touched down to the ground, my feet hit the ground first, and I kept rolling and tumbling on the ground.

As I opened the door, there stood a tall dark strong handsome man. I said his dad, and he said that he was tired and hungry. He went straight to the living room to talk to my mother, and they seemed to be talking in secret of something very important.

I remember a wormhole. I was with a young lady pulling to our side of the wormhole some type of large gun; the people on the other side of the wormhole could see the gun disappear. As we pulled the whole gun over to our side, a light over the wormhole went out.

My father had gone to the nightclub that had a jazz band playing. When I went in, the man said that he had got so drunk that they had to put him out, and he directed me to where he was; he was in a truck sleeping. I woke him up. I had a great feeling for him. He started the engine to the car.

A small fast jet attached to a large steel shipping container ascended into the air on a 45-degree angle and kept going higher and higher until it started to descend lower and lower. The fast jet finally touched down to the runway and detached itself from the huge steel container. The steel container swirled over the container. A large passenger airliner was taking off and just lifted right over the swirling steel container, just missing hitting it by seconds. Also a large passenger bus swirled around the steel container to miss it. Both vehicles didn't keep on going to their destination; they returned to the starting point. A rescue team was sent out, and a young black man stopped the container, and his mother congratulated him.

I was invited to a great dinner party in a five-star hotel that I was also staying in. But I had forgotten my ticket with my sister and wife; in my room, I tried on many combinations with my maroon pinstripe suit, but none of them satisfied me. The cleaning ladies came into my room to clean and took one of my garments. I tried to think of the number to call my sister or wife but didn't remember; I also left my identification with them. When I got out of the car, I left my ticket with them too.

I was tried to get to large festival but didn't have a car, then I saw someone with a car that I knew. The person was male friend of mine and he was going to the same festival, so he gave me a ride. We ran out of gas, then a woman driver pulled up and got off her car; she said that she was also going to the same festival, but she had ran out of gas also. We looked around for a gas station, but they all seemed to be closed; in fact, one closed right as I looked at it.

There were groups of gentleman betting at high stakes on just a secret technique of two professional boxers; the bet was to see if they could cause one fighter to reveal his technique before the actual fight, so these gentlemen caused a tussle between the two fighters, and he did reveal his secret technique. The big money men paid off the main people in the bet and only allowed one fighter to dance at the fight.

I was sitting comfortably with my companion; she was holding me closely with affection. As we watched the other lovely women dance rhythmically and hypnotically, she held my hand softly and told me she loved me and kissed me gently; I said the same to her.

In the twilight, I ran swiftly through the country town, on an empty dirt road, and no one was around. I looked for dogs, but there were none. I thought I saw a woman get into her car in a parking lot somewhere above me. So I just took off running with speed and strength; my spirit felt iridescently free and light as an eagle. I was nude and felt so good, but when I reached the residential area of the country road, a school bus went zooming by, and then I stopped.

There were a group of men who were led by one man who knew me. They were some type of task force; the leader said I was good at what I do and would be traveling with them. They wore plain gray or neutral-colored suits; there were over a dozen of these men. They seemed to be on a mission, capturing something or finding a solution to a sinister problem. I was very happy to know them. They seemed to be from another place or higher dimension.

As I took a shower, I wondered why my girlfriend had not come home. I got out of the shower and went to her and went throughout the house, then I heard someone in the shower. I called her name, but she did not answer. I looked in the shower and noticed the lady in the shower was not my girlfriend, then I walked to the living room and saw my girl standing right in front of me. She said that she was sorry, but that she couldn't help not answering me.

Many runners and people from all over the world were in this city. We got off the plane and took a taxi to the part of the city where we were going to stay. Fortunately, we already had a key for our room, which was room 9. My brother immediately took a run in the park. There were so many people around when I opened the door to the room. I asked them a question, but no one answered. I went to the manager; he talked about how black people were some of the best runners in the world and that I should try to win the race. I assured him that I had run many marathons and I would do well. The manager showed me another room that I could stay in; it looked wonderful.

We were in a sports hall, communicating to each other about the contest that was much similar to golf, then we walked down the stairs to cafeteria to get some drinks. As we walked, I noticed how everything felt so real that I could not tell the difference between the world in my awake state or dream state. I wanted to ask one of the other sport people where we were. I thought to myself maybe Wisconsin, but I did not see any sign on the wall as to where we were. We finally had a drink; it seemed so real that I didn't feel it was a dream at all.

The boxer showed me or the other fighter the secret technique; some other well-known gentlemen had place a high bet that they would force him to show the secret technique before the fight. Another fighter would try to get him angry before the fight to show the hidden technique. The boxer fell for it, and in the middle of a scuffle, he showed the secret technique. The well-known gentlemen got paid off generously, and only one fighter was allowed to dance at the fight and only dance.

The people were not responding when I talked about getting a ticket. The stewardess seemed not to notice my presence. Three or four other ladies were making fun of me. I thought they were disrespecting me, so I gave them a lecture on how I respected other races and they even tried to touch me in a playful manner with their hands. We went to get on the plane, but I thought of the plane crashing, then the plane fell apart.

I rode a brand-new silver-plated bicycle around a lovely city, listening to beautiful live music, oldies but goodies, and I was riding nude. When I totally realized that I should put some clothes, I went into a house and put some clothes on, and when I came out, the brand-new silver-plated bicycle was gone.

I was seeing a unique image of my face looking back at my face several times and saying to myself, "Are you Mr. Jones? Are you Mr. Jones?" I finally woke up out of the dream, only to realize that I had pants around and covering the top of my head; my head felt very warm, as I took the pants off my head.

Then I searched around my bedroom for a long slender martial arts pole and I found one. I started doing movements with my whole body and the pole. I could feel the magnetic energy tug on the pole in every direction I moved it. I finally took the movements of the pole into another room, but I had to stop because the pole came to close to my oldest sister's feet. She had been cooking breakfast for herself. I could see the hot circular pancakes and eggs in the frying pan; they looked so good, but I told her I wanted peanut butter and jelly sandwiches. I looked in the refrigerator but saw none. I went to see who was on the phone; it was off the hook. I picked up the phone and heard a voice say hello, then I hung the phone up, and then I realized my sister was standing across the street looking at me. As I looked out the window, I saw a large angry dog running after some people barking. The owner stood with his whole body on top of the dog's neck, but the dog was still barking and angry. I yelled at my sister to take precautions, and she walked up some steps, but the dog came after her and started to bite her on her right arm. The owner finally got the dog away from her, but she had been bitten several times. I could hear her arguing with the owner. I tried to run out the house to help her.

As I looked down the road, the people on the road looked frozen, like statues; they had stopped moving in various poses and gestures. Far away from this scene, there on the side of a hillside city road, I helped a sleeping man wake up by pulling him up by his arm. At that moment, I looked at the road where the people had stopped moving, and all of a sudden, they started walking and moving. The man who I helped to wake up, I knew that he knew something about this and also I knew he was a genius. I asked him what was going on, but he told me nothing. Then I saw a wise man with his family; he said hello to me in a very friendly manner.

I had to take a test with lots of other people I didn't even know and had no pencil, so I asked a lady for one. She gave me one, but then she wanted to whip me. I told her that was not going to happen; some other women who were in a group seemed to be looking on and smiled when I said that. Taking hold of the black whip, I told her you're not even supposed to whip animals. Somehow, I needed to get a chair to take the test, so one the ladies gave me a chair and caught up with the rest of the group who were going to take the test.

In this world, I was in a house and a person outside the house wanted to come into the house without my permission. He tried everything to get into the house. I heard him at the door; the first time he knocked, I opened the door but kept the inner screen door locked, but the next time he knocked, I tried the same thing, but it didn't work totally. So he got in. He tried to eliminate me, but I finally got away from him because he began to transform and secondly because I went through a solid wall with some type of magical force and appeared in another place. I felt like a powerful magician who used his secret invisible powers. I was in a world of giant moving tulip plants with heads like tulips that ate anything in their path. I seemed to know how to not get eaten but to help them in eating other animals or plants that were in their path of movement, like a snake moving on the ground only with its head up. Some of these creatures were big and some were small. They could suck any-sized animal or plant through the head or flower part of the plant. I finally made my way to an abandoned, partly torn-down house that seemed to be in a hidden place that the creatures couldn't find. The fact was that these plants had destroyed this place a long time ago. There were various people there who looked very young, men and women, one seemed to be my guide; the people were telling me about these creatures. One lady wanted my guide to introduce me to her, but I didn't seem to notice her desire, so the lady asked me what's my name and I said Calvin.

The beautiful black woman took me to her castle where another beautiful black woman gave me a gift in a wooden rectangular box. I didn't open it, but I thanked her for the gift. Her name was Monica, and she wanted me to kiss her, so I did and she was happy. There were other people in the castle, mostly men. I talked with them about moving to Trinidad and how many American dollars to their one. Was there land available? The women responded to my questions, but the men were into their own world.

I was in a house with a beautiful lady, my oldest brother came in to congratulate her, and then I found that she was talking to a beautiful little girl. The beautiful little girl started to cry when she saw me. I was wrapped in a beautiful colorful cloth that the beautiful lady gave me. I told the little girl that she knew me; she stopped crying for a moment and then continued to cry some more.

There the frisky tan dog ran fast through the green country terrain and the other predator dogs came after the frisky tan dog. I could see it running through the natural settings, hills and valleys. But unfortunately, the predator dogs had gotten too close, so the frisky tan dog ran into someone's house. When it reached inside the house, there were two other dogs there, but they quickly turned into two people, man and woman. The frisky tan dog saw the other dogs sharpening their claws for the hunt. Then the frisky tan dog seemed to take its focus off the predator dogs and stared at the TV, which had some type of show on. As the frisky tan dog stared at the TV, it became more human-like, just like a young woman. The other two dogs in the house became a man and woman. The man began moving the furniture around in the house in different positions. Then he started talking with the woman in English. They were saying that they hope I get the hint. After he was finished moving the furniture in different positions, I noticed and focused on a picture that the woman had painted of a woman that was very large in a black-and-white-and-red-striped dress. All of us talked about the picture and gave our opinion of the composition and content and meaning of the picture.

CALVIN EARL DALLAS

The special group of people were learning tai chi. In a snowy land, the tall man's left foot seemed like it had been chopped off. I talked to him, but he seemed to be okay. His wife was not there with him. The soldiers from the snowy white land charged with a warlike sound. I started to run, as I saw them coming swiftly to the snow castle. When they got to where I was, I stopped because one of the warriors held up a sign for me to see; it basically said that whole thing was a joke or not real, and that they were just playing and having fun. It wasn't a real attack. One the soldiers followed me as I continued walking. I cursed him because he kept on following me, and he seemed to turn into a waiter serving drinks. Then he attacked me with a long pole. I blocked most of his hits, and I hit him under his armpit with my thumb. It seemed to cause him great pain by the look on his face. This slows his attack down to a halt.

The dark Spanish man asked me if I liked freaky sex. I said no; he said I wasn't a man if I didn't do freaky sex. His language seemed to be African and Spanish; I said I liked traditional sex. He and his people were also speaking a different language of Spanish and African, which I understood, but could only telepath in English. I sat down and watched from an audience; the dark Spanish man performed with his singing group. The electricity went off, but his group kept on singing. They sounded wonderful to rhythm.

I took by my own hands a large tan German shepherd–looking dog to a lady in her house because there was a man in the house who I knew could talk to the dog and probably get the dog from following and chasing me. The dog seemed to be magnetically attracted to me. The lady called her husband and told him that the dog would not stop following me, so the husband called the dog into the room that he was in. The dog grunted only once but didn't make another sound, as I heard the man talking to the dog and asking why it kept on chasing me. I had to continue to run because I somehow knew that the dog would continue to chase me. So I ran out of the house, and sure enough, the dog came after me again. I could feel him and see him; it was as though the dog had some type of mission or purpose to chase me. I saw that I could escape the dog by visiting a chain of restaurants that were high up in the air off the ground. The only way that I could get to them was to climb up to them or swing from a long chain; one time, two men tried to stop me, but their timing was to slow. I knew the dog could not climb. Each restaurant I went in had a small square opening for a door. I went through feet first; once inside I got a drink, I wanted to pay for it, but there was no one there. Deep down inside, I knew that the dog was still after me; he couldn't climb, but I could feel his intent.

I visited one of my deceased brothers who had left the earth. We were in a room in a city, and he talked about animals and insects being trapped in a house. I felt that his energy told me he was involved in the study of the science of magic. He seemed to be different in that way, more confident in his being. We had dinner together; he offered a vegetarian dish, which I enjoyed immensely, but I also noticed that he had a vegetarian dish also, but it seemed to be different from mine. We both were very happy and agreed to go to a nightclub after dinner. Then I had another dish of vegetarian food. As I was enjoying it, all of a sudden, a little girl walked into the room, and I called her a goddess.

I was Muhammad Ali, the famous champion of the world, and was waiting for my turn to fight in the ring; a motorcycle went buzzing by, and I had to lift myself out of the way because the road was too narrow. I had a small waiting room to wait in, but I didn't want to wait in there because it was too small and closed in.

I was at a big formal party; one lady who was the host went to get the wine. Out of the corner of my eye, I saw her drop the wine and the glasses. Then I met a different type of fellow; he kind of looked like a reptilian. I shook both of his hands; he told me that he would very much like to carry some more wine on his back and glasses.

I was in a place or a friend's apartment; he was watching me caress and kiss the breasts of a beautiful woman, and he was very happy and overwhelmed. Then when I came back to the same apartment, he wouldn't let me in but gave me a key to the door and said that I should build a new door downstairs.

As I walked through the city with my sister, I noticed the energy flow in my body was great. We talked about how our mother talked about multilevel apartment buildings, and I also told my sister that we could create our own planet. At one point in our walk, you can see landscape of the city getting higher. We could see asymmetrical buildings that looked like they were going to fall down. The alleviation of the landscape seemed to be getting higher as we got closer. But the asymmetrical buildings were perfectly balanced. We could feel the intense gravitational pull as we got closer to the asymmetrical buildings. The gravitational fields were too great for us, so we decided to turn back. As I urinated, my urine went straight across the room in a strong stream of energy, I was amazed at the power of the projection. I found a special book in the library; it had compartments that were like a pocketbook for money. But I noticed a gentleman in a very nice gray suit, who was watching me very carefully, so I looked at books apparently to throw him off. Then I went by him to look at books, and his energy or force fields propelled me away from him. When I was next to him, I tried to make like I was looking for some type of book, but the details on the book didn't seem to be in English or any other language. There were colors and geometrical symbols. The next thing I knew, he was coming after me. I finally let him catch me, but he didn't know that I had a gun. I held it to his chest, not pulling the trigger yet, then to his neck, as I pulled him closer; before I could pull the trigger, I fainted and collapsed. The man in the gray suit had been calm the whole time; as he came closer to me, I began to regain consciousness. He pulled out of his suit two long needles with some type of screw-like electronic structures on top of both of them. As he manipulated those structures with the thump and longest finger of each hand, the needles seemed to get longer. All of a sudden, the room seemed to fill up with police investigating the situation. I felt safe, but the man in the suit sprayed a large square in front of him of some type of gas, as he came closer to me with the needles. I hoped that the police would stop him, but the man disappeared or was cloaked somehow, but I could still see the needles and kept getting out of the way because it seemed like his target was my head. Suddenly, I was in an open park area with a lot of people, sitting down at tables like a festive occasion. I still had plenty of money. There was a little boy that I was responsible for; he had a very heavy chain attached to one of his legs, and at the end of the chain, there were some wheels attached. I tried to keep him near me, but he followed his father into a store. I had to catch him and I did. There was a person with me who had a large van to pick him up with. I told him where the boy was, but I got lost in the city and never got back to the man with the van to pick up the young boy.

We tried to leave out of a certain set of doors of the back of the church, but the doors were locked. We went out the front doors; as we passed through those doors, a beautiful light-skinned woman called my name, "Calvin." I looked at her; she was smiling, but I didn't know her. I could see her eyes and face; she had a lot of clothes on.

I met an old friend; he wanted to smoke marijuana. I told him no. I noticed that I had some sort of crystal in my pocket when I talked to him. I was going to find a particular McDonald's, but I lost my way looking for a certain professor. My old friend showed me a different set of new stores and a new McDonald's. I realized that the city had changed, with new places; perhaps I was in a whole new city.

I was running in a city, and I stopped because there was a large dark gray eagle gliding a couple feet over my head. There was a man inside his kitchen cooking some food, watching me dodge the eagle outside his porch window. The eagle seemed like it was trying to land on the top of my head. The man said the bird was trying to tell me something; it changed its shape into a colorful iridescent colorful spinning disc, the color of a hummingbird. The man and I looked at vast number of highways and vehicles in traffic from his porch. I told him I needed to find a park to run in. Gently, I stepped off his porch over many shoes and other gadgets. At the bottom of the porch were three young men who were just standing there talking among their selves. I talked with them about fierce animals. As I left them and started to run down the street, a man and woman in a black sports car called my name, "Calvin." I remember them from somewhere. I went across the street to where they were. I wanted to shake their hands. The woman was tall, slender, and blonde she was excited to tell me what she and her mate were saying that she and her husband had been touched. I really had a feeling that I didn't want to see what she was going to show me.

Students kept running away because they were afraid of something in the park that they couldn't see.

There were four of us disciples of tai chi. Our master, a great tai chi master, consoled us on the deepest aspects of tai, staying focused with meditation of the heart. As I talked to my great master of tai chi, I noticed that his face was very black and almost a different texture of skin, not of this earth. He wanted to know where the fourth disciple was and how he been allured away by and with a beautiful woman. I resisted the temptation. I never told him exactly where he was; I just said he had gone.

The woman was so soft; she wouldn't let me go. My brother was playing in the band a tune on his saxophone. The lady started to play on some type of reed instrument. She looked at me and asked me if I was ready to play and I said yes; she came over to me and gave me the instrument. There was a piece of her hair on the mouthpiece. I took the hair out of my mouth and asked her jokingly where had she been to have this hair on her mouthpiece. Then she took the instrument away from me. After that, she curled softly her whole body around me, hugging with tender singing to me. She didn't want to let me go. I wanted to play the instrument that she had given to me but couldn't. As she caressed me tenderly, I looked at my brother and saw that he was still focused on his playing. I looked at him several times. She was so sweet and nice; I sensed that she could be a great wife for me.

I had been in this place before, an airport, waiting to pick up a ticket or a catch a ride on a jet going to a familiar location; it has the same familiar background. Sometimes, I catch the jet, but the location is nowhere. I can see it in my mind's eye.

I was the star of the show. There was a beautiful, tall, cream-colored, and slender woman who came to me and wanted me to go to a place with her after the show. I talked to her, but she could hardly make her words audible, but I could understand her anyway. She led the way; I held her hand tightly in an awkward way. The next thing I realized was that I was being photographed by her and a group of people in an open moving pickup truck; they were all standing up taking my picture as I walked down the road. I took frontal poses as I walked. I could see the environment around me so vividly, the green in the plants, the people and their faces looking at me. Finally, I saw and felt the blue sirens of the police up ahead, and I knew something was wrong. There were a lot of men in suits telling everything was okay, but for some reason, the lady was gone and the other photographers weren't there. So I went back to the theater where I was a star. When the director had heard from me what had happened, he went to one man and started choking him, then I knew it was not the man whom he was choking who had set me up. It was a tall strange man in the next room. When I looked at him, he came after us with a gun that shoots screws, but as he pointed it at us, it didn't work, so he tried to poke me with a screw in the chest. At that point, I jumped up and threw a flying kick to his head.

I was walking in a place or neighborhood that looked like a part of a city in the States. One person, a Rasta was walking coolly and saw me and said a greeting. I tried to catch up to him; he said he had some great smoke and that he knew I wanted a quarter pound. He gave me some to try; it had a very dark color, almost purple. I put some in my mouth. I couldn't taste it, but it felt very strong. He said he was waiting for a shipment to come in. We arrive at a spacious house, where there was a large family dining. The people dining referred to me as the king who has arrived. I noticed my clothes were our traditional garb, and then I started to comb my hair before I entered their home. As I sat down, the women gave me a variety of foods to eat, but I noticed that some of the women left. My plate that the food was on kept lifting off the table. I tried to hold it down, but it kept raising up, so I asked a lady next to me why this was happening and said that my sister was jealous of me.

One of my old friends showed me beautiful homes in green gardens and meadows. She talked about the southern and northern parts of the city. As I sang a song about bananas, elementary students showed me a long lime-green snake in his hands.

I was in my girlfriend's house; she wanted me to buy some white ginseng for her. So she gave me a lot of dollars: tens, ones, twenties. I took the money from her and started to go to the store; as I was leaving the house, I saw three European men walking toward me. I heard one say he is a nice guy, then he said, "Hi, Calvin." I say hi to him as well. Then I continued to walk to the store. I noticed some puddles of water in front of me; as I was walking, I stepped into one, and to my surprise, I sank and was submerged in more than ten feet of water; apparently, I was walking with some several books on ginseng in my hand. They sank almost to the bottom. I retrieved them quickly and got out of the water, but I didn't really feel wet.

As I was coming back to my girlfriend's house, I noticed that the three men I had seen earlier were sitting in her house relaxing. The man who said hi to me and knew my name was a famous action adventure movie star and was also the father of my girlfriend. He told me that I should get the product residual.

I was in a room that was very detailed in color, pattern, and design; one gentleman was in the room with two usual-looking trumpets. I felt that this was not a dream at that moment; it was like I was as consciously aware of life as when I was awake. I asked the gentleman why didn't he play the trumpet. We both took hold of the two trumpets but didn't play them still.

I was waiting in city to get a city bus, then a bus was passing me by and the bus driver started to bring the bus close to me, but I didn't want that one so he drove off. Then I saw another bus coming; it stopped. Other people and I who were waiting also for this particular bus started to get on; it seemed as though this bus had disappeared. We couldn't find the door. We started to go up the stairs but in another building. Then we finally found the door. We started to go into to the bus to meet the driver who was collecting the money; there was a clown entertaining the crowd while everyone paid their money. The clown made funny expressions and gestures with his whole body. After I paid the driver, I went to sit down in a seat and noticed there were no seats next to the windows, so I sat next to a young woman, and eventually, she moved to another seat, but I didn't see her move. All I know is that I looked up and she was in a different seat. There were some waitresses who brought us a cupcake-like food. I ordered some type that was different; they didn't understand what I said, but the driver made sure they heard it and they gave me the cupcake, but I don't remember eating it. Then the driver came and sat with the passengers as we ate; the next thing I realized, the driver was sitting at a table with his back turned to me not to far away from me. I could see and hear him eat only from the back. He ate viciously. I could hear the extreme crushing sounds and tearing and ripping of whatever he was eating with fierceness. I looked around and noticed if anyone else noticed this, but everyone on the bus seemed to ignore, or it didn't bother them, so I just remained calm.

There was only one bully child who started to poke the children with nails. So I stopped him and took the nails away from him. He lived in a certain neighborhood that was controlled by certain officials; I went to talk to one of the main officials with the other children who were being abused. We walked up a long flight of stairs; we went in a room where he was, and I basically told him that the children and I wanted safe passage through a certain and particular neighborhood. We waited a long time for his decision, even though he was still in the same room; finally, he said yes. We walked up another long flight of stairs again until we finally came to a monumental-size black deck, overlooking a midnight sky. It seemed to be a deck of a navy vessel; there were many officers on the deck who saluted to us as we walked by. In fact, one asked me how the ladies are.

He even knew my name. I seemed to recognize him as someone I knew in high school, but now he was an officer. Now we came to a part of the vessel where we were told by a group of officers, one female, that we had to go into the inner part of the vessel; they gave us detailed directions. I also noticed that one of the officers had a vest in his hands. I started to feel close in.

I was on a great ship that was docked on the deep water of some rocky city. There were many black people on the ship; you could see from the inside how vast the city was, and it was deep with water from the inside and outside. A lady was with me who seemed to be a wife of mine from a long time ago. She wanted to cook some food for us; the older women who usually cook all the food on the ship said it was okay. As she started to cook the food, I walked around to see the rest of the ship. I noticed that the ship started to move with great speed. At that moment, I felt as if the city was a huge rocky crater with deep water channels. I looked out the window and noticed that the water was up to the lower part of the window ledge, but the water didn't flow in the ship. I told one man I had to come up for air because it seemed that the ship had transformed into a submarine, with one opening to come up to see the water surface. So when I came up, I saw that the anchor had been dropped, and we were already secure to the dock, so the ship or submarine came to a halt. As I stood up through the opening, I could see that we landed in a majestic part of the deep-water rocky crater city.

I used the technique of gesture drawing to capture the movement of the people living in the outside streets. It felt like a storyboard. My assistant, my beautiful girlfriend, went with me, I had a large drawing pad of white paper, which I had to hold with two hands because it was so large. With a lead pencil, I drew people walking, talking, laughing, while my girlfriend held the drawing pad. I drew very rapidly the form and shape of buildings, plants, people, with flash-quick movements of the pencil. After I had finished the gesture drawing, we started to discuss the project; my girlfriend walked over to one of the houses that was on the same street we had been drawing on and knocked on the door. I knew that my ex-wife was in that house, and I wondered why my girlfriend did that. I didn't want to see my ex-wife, but when she came to the door, I introduced my girlfriend to her. Before the other person in the house could get to the door, my girlfriend and I left. As we walked back up the street that we had been drawing on, we realized that this was a neighborhood where there was a special school for talented and creative children. The street was full of creative genius children.

A large muscular man got me in a headlock, full nelson, but I relaxed totally and he never put pressure on me. Several times, we rolled on the ground and still never put pressure on my neck and head because I just would relax and wait for the pressure. So then he said he wanted a match with me. I agreed. He had some friends with him, a young lady and a man. I went home to get ready for the match. I lived in a high-rise apartment building on a high floor. I noticed in my room I had a brand-new gun that was still in its new package. I started to tear the package open. Then a young man knocked on the door. I opened it for him. He said that he wanted to show me some martial arts. I asked him what type. He said a mixture, then he showed me the same gun; he had one too. All of a sudden, there was someone at the window. I went to see who it was and it was the young man's girlfriend. She was nude without any clothes on. So we got ready to leave. An old man stopped by my door; as he finished walking up the stairs and called my name, he said that he wanted me to teach him. I told him maybe another time, but he insisted on now. So I just left with the young couple for my match.

I was in a moving car with a lady, but the front window was very dark. I tried to fix it so that we could see out of it clearly. But it didn't clear up; we could only see outside the windows. As I looked out the side window, I saw a man jump on a horse from a running position. The horse tried to throw the man off, but he couldn't. The horse jumped over a car with the front hood open where the engine was. The horse's hind legs got stuck in the engine area. The car engine was still on and running. The horse kept kicking its hind legs; I thought they had got cut off. Finally, it jumped and loosened its hind legs for freedom. The horse ran swiftly up the highway until the man did get off and ran to get a horse saddle and even ran faster than the horse to get back on the horse to saddle it; by this time, the horse was running with two heads, one in the back and one in the front. After that, I met the man who was riding the horse at his house. I was very excited to see this short kind of thick man. I told him he ran faster than a sixty-minute quarter mile; he just smiled and invited me to dinner. We walked down some stairs to dinner to a house under his, but it was spacious, not closed in. We heard people talking behind a wall or hidden door. Somehow, it seemed as though we were way under the ground. I didn't mind; I felt comfortable.

As I cut down various vegetation in the area I was living in, I saw a man walking past me with a supreme haircut that made him look so majestic and full of energy.

I was at a dinner, eating and drinking with people I knew; one gentleman said that I had called on him for help in the past when I was in trouble, but I told him I didn't remember it.

Two dogs came after me; they were very large and black. I ran to a building that had a high line or bar extending across it and climbed up on it. When the dogs got to me, they tried to jump up and get me, but every time they did, I would pull myself up higher than them. They couldn't get me, so they finally changed into two beautiful black women. Somehow, there was a man with

CALVIN EARL DALLAS

them; the women left me alone, but I grabbed the man by his throat and choked him until he became unconscious.

In a certain place, a wise man gave me detailed instructions. Then a lovely lady walked over to me and embraced me; she spoke to me in Spanish.

The lady teacher took me into a classroom where she let me look at a special document, and then she gave me some food. Another woman teacher came in and I hid the document temporarily, then the lady teacher who let me see the special document first hid it permanently.

I was attending a school at the university; it had classes, and the professor told my oldest brother to come to me and asked me if I wanted to go to a party, and I said yes. But I was somehow in a situation with a woman whose car had broken down. The police had stopped; they asked her for her identification, and they searched through everything in the car. I helped the lady put everything back in the order that they had gone through. Finally, the police let her go. She got into the car and drove off. Another strange man in another larger geometric metallic vehicle drove off behind her. Then the police asked for my identification. I showed it to them, and they said I was a good person to help the lady out but to be careful. He was talking to me with his hand on my shoulder. Another police walked me to house on Seventh Street, where we both sat down in the back of the house on the patio, and we talked; he told me that he would put some documents in a container on this area. Then we walked to the police station, I pointed out some new modern architectural building downtown to the police that I had never seen before. They were made from a colorful glass-like material and were tall and monumental. At the end of our walk, he told me to be strong and gave me a very strong hand grip as I left him. I felt loved and helped by my new friend.

I was in a place where I was walking in the park and I had to go to the bathroom, and there were two gentlemen who were watching me. In fact, one was even smiling at me, and then I noticed that he seemed to know me, and then I put my waste into a garbage container on the street. I founded myself back into a bathroom on the toilet, but this time, I could see the two gentlemen talking, but they weren't looking at me and there were no walls in this bathroom. So I finally did my waste in the toilet; this time when I did, someone came to inspect the garbage container.

The whole university was falling apart; the campus dorms and the classrooms were in combustion and confusion. It was as if an earthquake had shaken everything loose; the students were trying to gather what they could to leave the campus. The whole place looked like a broken, shattered puzzle. The police were all around, trying to maintain some type of order in the midst of an invisible bomb with visible results. I walked right past them into some of the buildings to see nothing but disorder. The buildings seemed to be falling apart and people were trying to get away.

We were trapped in a series of 3-D images that were elevators; every time we got off one of those elevators, the next would come a different direction, high or low, east, west, south, north, and the interior of the elevator would be small sometimes or large. I saw people sliding on their knees into a small opening just big enough for their own bodies. I saw several elevators open up at the same time with different floor levels and various interior sizes. The wall of these elevators seemed to be made out of a certain type of metal with a soft material like cotton stuffed inside of their walls. Getting on to one of these elevators was very tricky because they were all around you, coming and opening up at the same time; there was no building at this point, only interior and exterior elevators. Then all of a sudden, I was outside, watching a beautiful blonde lady get out of a car and start to walk; as she walked, it seemed as though I knew her, she was wet, like she had just taken a shower. She walked on a park trial in an open green area; the sun was shining brighter. I ran after the lady, but when I got to her, she started to tell me about another lady who was walking on the same park trial. I could see her; she was smiling and pregnant; also, she was watching me very closely. I didn't know this pregnant lady. I forgot all about the first lady with the wet hair; she seemed to be not there anymore. I had a good feeling about the pregnant smiling lady.

Now I was moving slowly in a circle, walking, counterclockwise and clockwise, tai chi and bagua movements, thinking of pressure points and internal energy; when I was finished, I heard an audience clapping loudly. I was very humble and shocked because I didn't see anyone. A beautiful young lady who worked for the church said I should join her full-time, but I said I had two jobs, a full-time and a part-time.

I was asleep in a house where other people were sleeping also. I saw a lady friend of mine with her boyfriend get up and go to another part of the house; at first, she argued with him, then I saw her open her top garment so that he could kiss and caress her breasts gently with his tongue. I made like I was still sleeping when they came into where I was. I could feel her lie down next to me; her body felt slender, soft, and feminine, and I could feel her boyfriend watching me closely. Her boyfriend was upset that she slept next to me, but he didn't bother me. She stayed by me for some time, then she got up and left with her boyfriend. Then I got up and I saw my oldest brother inter the room; also my lady friend came back into the room and went to an envelope and took out a lot of paper bills. She gave this money to my brother and told him to put it in the bank. My brother left, and she came to me and gave me some money also. I put it inside my clothes.

I was woken up by the smell of my friend's delicious cooking eggs. I could actually smell them; before that, I was somehow outside, looking up at the dark night sky. There was a message of bright yellow and white words through the dark night sky. I could only read so much because it kept disappearing so fast. I could see the date 1777 and other information directed to me.

—m—

I was with a beautiful woman in bed; we woke up and made love, but it seemed as if my brother was under another bed in the same room. Somehow, I saw another woman and said excuse me and went to talk to the other woman; she showed me where she lived. Then I saw many houses and people in this neighborhood. The woman started to walk in the water, and I told her not to walk in the water and corrected my Spanish.

I went to see Louis; he was in the living room working on his TV and some other mechanical device. It seemed as though he had just moved into this place.

I sensed that he had broken up with his female companion. His teenage daughters came in; Louis introduced them to me. I felt joy meeting his daughters and their friends. But one of their male friends wanted to stare me down, so I stood my ground and stared at him back. Then he just smiled and tried to put a crumpled piece of paper down the front of my sweatshirt. I took the crumpled paper from him and put it down inside the back of his shirt. Then he just smiled and went upstairs with the daughters and the other male. Then I went out on the porch where Louis was preparing a special soup. I sat in front the table where he was preparing the soup.

The soup was an earth-red tone with pink and red beans in it and various vegetables. He kept on turning the soup with a big spoon. Before this happened with the soup, Louis had said he had a special kung fu video for me to watch. But he said he didn't want me to copy the style of the kung fu in the video, but he wanted me to create my own style. I also agreed with him. As he was preparing the soup for me, two very traditional African American ladies came on his porch. I greeted both of the ladies but shook the hand of only one. That particular one asked Louis questions about the soup with laughter. Louis kept adding more ingredients to the soup as she talked to him; he even got really happy and was dancing. As he mixed and turned the soup, he kept smiling at me. All of a sudden, Louis gave me an envelope that I could see through and there was lots of money in it. Next Louis and I, with the two Afro American ladies, were riding in red convertible on the road. Louis was driving the red convertible; in the back seat, I was holding hands with the lady that that I shook hands with. The money in the envelope was pinned on the top of the front seat in the middle.

I was in my bedroom in a kind of apartment, and my brother, who was one year younger than me, was returning with a lot of boxes on my bed. I really didn't want all those boxes on my bed. Then he gave me one of the boxes. I felt that it was a present. I told him thank you even before I opened it up. Then I opened the box; it was a pair of shoes, colored black and tan. I put the shoes on; they seemed to be very heavy but quite supportive. But I still didn't want all those boxes on.

I walked up the mountain and saw workers along the way, black men with machetes; one wanted to chop my foot, then I got to a place where I climbed up a ladder and had to wait because some little girl was coming down the ladder.

I was in a group in a large hall. Everyone was meditating; the group leader was in front of us. A gentle happy man, he seemed to be telling, regulating, and observing everyone in progress. There was a lady and some man behind me saying something that was a chant; of course, it sounded good, but I didn't comprehend it. I stood up three times in a standing position to meditate at the back of the group. The third time I was at the theta state of brain rays, deep, deep, relaxation. I realized love is the ultimate state of meditation.

I was bought a new pair of shoes by this beautiful lady whom I had always admired and known, but she never would go out with me. She bought them with her own money. I put them on, and they felt so great. I told her that I felt that I could run superfast. She felt my feet while they were inside the shoes with her hand on top of the shoe. I wanted to give her money, but she had a vibration that it was okay or cool. We ran past a nightclub; I wanted to go in for a drink but kept running.

I said hello to various women teachers. I was walking to my room in the school, and there was a woman who I went to her classroom that had no air conditioner. I thought about teaching geography in 2-D and 3-D forms while in my classroom. The sun was very bright; you could see the teachers and parents very clearly; they were all women.

I was invited to a man friend's parents' house; he wanted to get ready so that we could go out on the town.

While he was preparing himself, I was looking around his parents' house. Then I met his father who was cleaning; his name was Chris. He seemed to have products to sell to me, but Chris had shown me some products like robots; his father showed me vitamins.

I was in cafeteria getting a lot of food, but I never got to eat the food.

I was sweeping an area and cleaning an area with a lot of water.

Someone stole my clothes that I had washed in the laundry. I couldn't find them, and then I found myself kissing a teacher in my school.

As she walked with me, I realized that she was another man girlfriend, but she still kissed me tenderly several times and told me that she loved me. The tender lady, a beautiful blonde, she walked so closely with me for a while, and then she left the party. I saw a young couple dancing, so I started dancing with funny gestures by myself while looking at them; the bartender gave me a look as if to stop making fun of them so I stopped. The boyfriend of the beautiful blonde girl appeared, so I went up to him and told him that he had to get his lady and paid more attention to her; as I talked to him, he was observing a ring that was on my finger, kind of gold, small, and round with little bit of the primary colors in it. I started to look at the hand and the ring too, but I had no idea what the ring symbolized. The party door opened up and the beautiful young slender blonde with some of her friends walked into the party. I notice that her blonde hair was now dark blue and short; she was very happy. As I watched her, she didn't seem to be there to look for her boyfriend.

I lost my way on a road in a cave. Then I was picked up by two men in a helicopter and placed in the back of a convenient shop that I could remember where I was. Now I was in a type of college school that I was spying on and I had a partner. I bumped into one officer who turned into a bird, just his face; I noticed he started to curse.

As I looked into the stillness of the dark blue sea, I saw a large black passenger boat emerge out of the sea slowly and gently; it grew in size, then it changed into a large pickup truck, then after it had driven a short distance on the road, it changed into a small classic black sedan. The driver got out and went to talk to another driver who had stopped his car and got out; they were dressed in black.

I had a store in town; the children came into the store and robbed the items in the store, and then they ran. I ran after them. I noticed that there were many people walking up the streets. I didn't catch them; they were having a lot of fun. In my place, one lady friend had given me a lot of plants on a special rack that extended throughout the apartment; the one pipe that was unattached flooded the apartment with lots of water. I finally got the water out by using buckets.

The setting was a familiar room where I traveled to all through time, but every time I get to the room, the people who live there or in the area would be different, but I would have the feelings of this one room for a long time. Also the room's appearance itself would change.

I was in a setting where an old lady was crossing a street. I went to help her because I saw a fast car coming; it was in the night then when the person in the car saw me helping the old lady cross the street. The car stopped about seventy five yards from where we were. After we got across the street, the car started up and pulled away at a normal speed.

A soldier went to a castle tic and slipped it open with his bare hands and took out another soldier and held him in his arms; the soldier he was holding had armor on and looked exactly like him. So when the soldier who was holding the other soldier saw this disappeared and went into the cast tic of the soldier who was pulled out. When in the cast tic, he smiled, then he went to sleep.

The beautiful young lady left her husband in awe because she had died all of a sudden; I looked into his eyes and gave my sentimental regard humbly. He acknowledged me with a knowing look of despair, and then he got up and went somewhere. I saw his lovely wife lying there so still and soft that in my soul, I had a hope that she would come back to life. After some moments passed, she begins to yawn, and she sat up and was kind of awake. I went closer to her and asked her how she felt; it took her some moments to reply, but she finally answered and said okay. I suggested to her that she give her husband a call. She got up and started walking briskly outside; I quickly followed a medium distance behind her. I saw her husband walk right into her path; he seemed to be asking her what had happened to her.

Some kind of dog-like animal was mad at me because I thought in my head that I didn't like the way the dog looked. I tried to talk to the dog, but it came after me and I tried to drown the dog under the water, but the dog wouldn't drown.

I was watching a boxing practice where different boxers were trying out their skills.

I went to a college school that had various classes. I had a dorm room to a mansion; outside were beautiful gardens that ran through. I tried to go back to some classes, but I couldn't find my way.

I had lost my way as I walked. I saw great buildings, beautiful country green and lush temples with holy monks singing; a little boy told me that they had said I had died in a fire that had burned down a hotel That was the last night that I had been staying with my friend. I had left there the other day to see a famous doctor. Not too far away in a great complex of buildings. I never got to see him. I went by the burned-up hotel,

Fearing that my friend had died in the fire, as I tried to get back to the great complex of the doctor's office. I notice the beautiful green country with many different people. One tall white strange-looking man came from out of nowhere, and someone was looking for me down by the water. It was my friend working on the top of some type of trees. He came down, and I hugged him and I almost cried. I was so happy to see him still alive. He said he was partying when the fire happened somewhere else at a nightclub in the night.

I was in a supermarket shopping, but I saw my father; he told me he would wait for me and give me a ride when I got finished. There was also another friendly man who said he would be very happy to give me a lift or ride, I told him I was okay, and then he said, "Are you going to stay out of the way?" I said yes. I saw a man trick another man into letting him go by blowing some type of black dust on his face. The man fainted after the black dust was blown on his face. The other man got away. Now he and two other men went through a dark long passageway that had their 3-D faces on the passage walls. The faces were very bright, protruding from the wall. In fact, one of the faces talked to one of the men who looked like it, to warn him of danger ahead. One of the men finally got away from his attacker and changed his shape back to his normal looking self by cutting off some thick and rough skin with a sharp knife. He also straightened out a crooked leg.

I was with a young beautiful lady with a white dress, and she wanted to dance. I said I will dance with you. So I held her hands and we started to dance in a nightclub where the DJ announced my name and that I was married to her. At first, we danced by ourselves to various jazz rhythms, and then we danced around in a large circle with other couples around chairs and tables. She told me to never give up on her. I told her sometimes the negative can be positive formation, even though we know that evil is trying to destroy the world. As we danced, I said let me give you an example. Plant a lotus seed in mud and you will get beautiful butterflies and flowers. Before I could give her another example, a tiny little dog started barking very loud and violently, then he started to run swiftly and everyone froze in their dance steps; the little tiny dog came over to me and bit my shoe heel off with giant crush. Then everyone in the place said my name in a hush, "Calvin," with some concern. I stayed calm as I felt something rush up my arm toward my head, then I woke up.

There were many people standing in line for tickets for the great show, but I was with a group of people who got in free. We went behind the stage and saw the area where the performers dressed. I wanted to go to the bathroom, and there were so many. I saw a man dressing up as a woman, then I saw him again and he said you never know what you can be until you try it out. The group I was with never really saw the main show; we just explored backstage.

I was in a large university in the library; I had made some type of picture on the wall. The librarian wanted to change it. I told her no, and then she told me I should do a project with *National Geographic* magazine, so I agreed. I tried to find the magazine in the library but couldn't find it.

I was treading the movie machine with a type of yarn; it was wet but the audience waited patiently, then I went to ask the brother of the brother who made the film if the film will dry after I had wrung it out.

I thought the wetness would mess up the machine, so yes, it was to dry. So he told one of his younger brothers to go and get all the film with the same wetness. I never got to see the real show or the film.

I was practicing my tai chi steps when all of a sudden, I felt something in the air. I looked out my door and saw two strange fellows, one was short and one was tall; they both gave me a feeling of pungent time travelers. They seemed to be very quiet and dense. But when I came outside, they walked hurriedly away in the other direction. I was in a place that I was a famous musician. I told one beautiful lady singer what could she teach me; she began to sing the part of the song that she wanted me to learn and saw myself.

Singing that part with her and another man, I had humble myself to learn something new. A group of other wannabe musicians wanted to take a ride in some limos that were handed down to me from a family legacy. There were two limos, both were black and long. They were in two separate rooms with closed doors. But when I opened the two doors, I saw the vehicles in place, then I closed the doors back.

I was with my mother. I told her I never hugged her enough when I was little, then I shuddered and almost cried when I hugged her affectionately, then she said you can't even kiss your mother, so I pulled some of her hair back out of her face and kissed my mother on lips. In another place, my mother told me I should fix my teeth and have them capped because I was getting older. I told her that she was thinking about me more, but in fact, I felt like I could tell her that I will live forever in a healthy body that won't grow old. I told her that I still felt young and that I want to live forever.

I was with two ladies and was trying to explain to one that I had to go see the other; they both were very beautiful and didn't mind that I was seeing them both of them. They were satisfied; I just had to make sure I could get to them both.

I went inside of a well-designed house and looked out the window; there were men fighting in the streets with knives, also there was someone hiding in the same house that I was in. I found him and knocked him out with one punch.

I was in a place of caves, in a lady of beauty cave. Her cave was very comfortable; she made love to me and me to her. Her body was very slender, long, and elegant, like the female human form but more like a mermaid, without the tail. She spoke perfect English. There was a man who walked by the cave and said something to her; we both knew that she had to leave the cave. She prepared herself to go. She said for me to get a basket of fruit for myself and that she could only see me on Thursdays and Tuesdays.

I was with my sisters. We were in a house upstairs; they were in a room talking to a girl, and I was in a room by myself just sitting on the bed.

I was at a party with lots of women. They were very beautiful; we, the men and women, were just relaxing and lounging. Then I started putting a lot of garbage into a garbage container that was overstuffed. Some men at the party were reading a book on how to cook a pizza.

We discussed the film; there was a beautiful couple, a lovely slender lady with her handsome man, and another handsome couple. I said that the common thread was how the Japanese had tried to capture and control Europe. The couples talked about how crazy the situation was; we looked out the window and saw various black dogs of different sizes and shapes with their home on the backyard grass. One of the lady had a long dress all the way down to her ankles; the dress was a silvery gold. She positioned her backside so close to me that I had to look at it and wonder if her man was looking at me.

I ran home after coming from a neighborhood where someone was killed by a snake. When I got home, everyone was sleeping, and my mother got up and out of bed; she told me in a frantic voice and motioning with hands that she told my grandmother that she had a dream of a snake following me to destroy me, but it didn't because I had redeemed myself.

There was a Rasta living in my mother's house; when I came late that night, I walked by him quietly. I could see that he was in the bed but not quite asleep yet. I said, "Excuse me." He nodded in a way that it was all right. Then I got some more money and put it my pocket. My mother and sister were up, and my mother told me to turn the light off in the TV room. But I told her the Rasta had just got up to watch TV, so she said okay. I told the Rasta to leave the door that went to the outside open so that I could come through it late at night. He said okay. I went to say goodbye to my mother, and she wanted me to kiss her. I noticed she had no top on and she had a tattoo on her upper body; she was very light skinned in color. Her skin was very young and tough. I gave her a kiss on her cheek, and it seemed to me she had been smoking a lot. I rubbed her on her back gently several times softly. I also gave my sister a kiss on the cheek and rubbed her softly and gently on her back. She was a little more elegant; she had no top on either. She told me to go because I could give her three babies by rubbing on her like that. My sister was light skinned too. The Rasta paid my mother some money for the rent.

I was trying to get to school on time, seeing the principal of the school talk to the kids; he was in a red shirt. I was almost to the school grounds, then I noticed I was running in the nude, so I hid behind a truck parked by the school grounds. I put on a large dashiki and some pants; the color was a kind of faded purple. When I came out from behind the truck, I noticed there was a group of well-dressed black women and men in suits and ties, sitting comfortably in chairs, watching me. There were about ten of them. I said good morning to some of them; one or two said good morning to me.

Another man and I had an assignment to complete; it was a certain formula to obtain information. A group of other teachers met for dinner in a hall, but none of these teachers felt like working on the formula or eating.

Another man and I were walking through a building that had so many intricate designs all over each and every wall. The man touched a wall, and it moved diagonally by itself to form a cubical elevator with geometrical symbols all over it. We entered inside of the elevator and the door. The man who was nonemotional held a device in his hand; it controlled the elevator, but the door did not open for us to get off, so I felt shut in, and I woke up out of the dream.

Somehow, I had gone to a house with two ladies: one was to be doing a homework assignment and the other one was a retired teacher who was dressed for a festival. As I sat there on the sofa, the one lady dressed for a festival was putting on and taking off lovely colorful sensuous lingerie; she even asked me to assist her, and at the same time, the other lady who was supposed to be doing a homework was also changing into sexy colorful garments.

At an art show, I communicated with many artists, some I knew and some I met for the first time. There were lots of men and women there; I was taking many pictures of the art and artists. The camera I was using was a classic. I had to load the film and setting for light, speed, and aperture. I didn't have a flash, so I used the natural light.

One of my favorite parents of the children at school was giving me a lift to school as I bathed in her car from a small gallon container of water. The route she was driving seemed to be long, but when she made a turn, I could see that the school was a couple of blocks right in front of me. But still her part was so far away from the school, I still thought I would be late.

I went to a club with a male friend but had no money. We looked inside. As we opened the door, we saw that it was an excellent exclusive dinner party club. Two well-dressed gentlemen came out of the club with their beautiful, smooth, curvy ladies. Then a drunken man staggered out saying words that made no sense; this was very embarrassing, then I found my friend had gone and was wearing a different outfit, black suit pants and suit coat with black, orange, and white small checks, with a cool checked dress hat with the same colors. It was nighttime, so as I walked down the sidewalk, the cars coming in my directions had very bright lights, so I tilted my checked dress hat over my eyes, as I walked down the street that night.

In a dining room area, there was a group of men watching a cartoon, but the sound was very low; we tried to make the volume get higher by working with the knobs and other devices externally, but it didn't work, then they put on a different movie that had some kung fu in it. My oldest brother was there trying to help me fix the problem. Then someone from school had hit or seemed to intent to hit a child with an insulated cord; he was smiling because he liked to discipline this way. We finally fixed the sound, but it sounded like it was coming from afar.

A policeman walked with me in the dark in the condominium complex; he said he was looking for a friend who lived in E1 or E10. I knew he couldn't have been in E10 because I lived in E10, so we went up the stairs. He said that he lived here in E1; he had the keys, so he opened the doors. I went back to my sister's condominium; she was talking on the phone. It was a dark night; there were many children at her home.

I took off my snow boots to go inside. Then all of a sudden, I was outside in the snow. I was throwing some small rocks on some large boulders that were standing up vertically in a cluster; each time some hit them, they would sink more into the earth and provide a stronger foundation. I made a pathway along the side of this formation in the snow like a small hill pathway in the snow.

I was in an advanced civilization that was having a virus attack on the air, there had been some people before who tried to store the air to freeze it, but now there was a foam-like substance taking the air from the planet. We had some small spray cans in our hands trying to neutralize the effect of the foam by spraying an antivirus lesser foam, but it wasn't working. All of a sudden, a man from nowhere who had a black tux blew up like a balloon out of the thin air. He said that he saw them in Atlantan civilization in his heart. "Now can we get along with it?" were his exact words.

I was in a girlfriend's home; she and I were downstairs, but somehow, another woman who liked me also was upstairs in the bedroom. I told the one upstairs that I had to go downstairs and see the one whose house it was, my girlfriend. When I got downstairs, my girlfriend wanted to make love to me. I was so turned on that I felt that I was going to explode, so she pulled out some protection, and as soon as she did that, her children woke up and came into the room with us, so I went upstairs to the other girlfriend. As I went upstairs, I looked back and saw that the girlfriend downstairs started talking on the phone to someone about what just happened. As I finally got upstairs to the other girlfriend, I felt like jumping out of the upstairs bedroom window to escape the situation.

As I sat in the stadium, I noticed that there were lots of women from my high school days who looked so pretty, but even though the years had passed by, they still looked young. There was a couple that sat next to me who I remembered, a man and lady. I looked at the woman, and she looked at me; what amazing joy did we feel after recognizing each other but saying not a word verbally.

There was a snake attacking me in a neighborhood by bouncing from tree to tree and flying through the air; as I was running, I had to look back and see if I could get out of the way before it attacked me.

I went into a building because I was lost in a new foreign city. A woman was there; I asked her how to get to some other part of town. She told me to go across the street and catch a bus named Shah Sheath Dar, Key and a man, who I knew in real life who was a librarian and also a runner and coordinator of official road races, talked graciously about the importance of art and gave me some brochures before I left. So I ran out the building and followed the lady's instructions to catch the bus. I saw the bus stop, so I ran to catch it, but it started moving again. I even saw the name on the side of the bus, so I missed it. But then I saw another lady who I asked about this same bus; she was going to take the same bus, so we both walked across the street to catch the bus at its designated spot. Before I got on the bus, I jumped on a bus-like vehicle and rode free of charge underneath the vehicle; it seemed to be carrying people inside of it on top. I rode this vehicle for some time, looking at the sights of the new city, the people, traffic, and sounds. A large truck toppled some merchandise out of it, then it stopped and some people got out to put the merchandise back in place and clean up the mess.

I had my own bread with me as I walked into the restaurant. I wondered would the Rasta lady cook me something nice to put inside of my bread, then she saw a friend who just fixed a curtain inside the restaurant. I was standing right next to it. The color was medium lime green and plastic but very cool. The Rasta lady fixed him some warm and nice food; she called his name so he went to her and got his warm dinner, but she wanted a kiss and he kissed her gently as I watched closely.

At the bottom level of a multilevel parking lot, I saw my father come out of his car. I called his name. "Hi, Daddy," as I looked through the car window at him. He walked from around the opposite side where I was to me; he seemed to be wearing all black. We shook hands for a long time, not too hard but just enough. I started talking to him, but all of a sudden, there was another young man who I had never seen before calling him Daddy also. My father said that they didn't tell him about the designs to the other man. Then there was a man and woman looking at another man who came into the parking lot trying to hide from them. At that, I told my father, "Let's get out of here." It took him some time to agree, but when he did, we went to the hotel next to the parking lot. The hotel was very tall and had many floors, so we took the elevator to the top. When we got to the top, we were in a beautiful outdoor garden that overlooked the city. The sunlight was bright, the green plants in the garden were so young, and the soil so brown and moist. We could see the greenest of the plants around the circumference of the building. We went into a room that had lot of windows and sunlight. My oldest brother started to have problems adjusting to the room; my mother was putting something over his head as we left the room. We decided to go back downstairs, but the elevator seemed too small, so I suggested that we walk down the stairs. As we walked down the stairs, you could feel the rhythm and the beat of the stepping on each stair, then all a sudden, a man appeared from out of nowhere and asked my oldest brother what was in the case he was carrying, so I opened the case and there was a trumpet and a flute in it. The man asked me if I could play the flute, and I said yes.

I asked a beautiful woman how she got in my dream, and she disappeared in a kind of colorful mist; I tried to grab her, with my hands, as the mist faded away.

I made a deal with a dog to give him some apples if he would stop nibbling and sniffing at my feet. As I talked to him, I noticed that his whole body had turned into a rectangular wooded box that was nothing but a huge mouth A man with a black suit on walked up to me and said, "Don't give him anything to eat."

My girlfriend walked closely with me, with her arm around me; she said that my hair was lighter. We were planning to meet each other in a church dorm room. We had figured out a secret knock on the door.

In bed, I had an out-of-body experience. It felt like I was vibrating down from a higher frequency and reentering my body, then I got up.

I had lots of money in my Bible; a friend of mine took me to his house. We talked about his wife. He was starting to fall asleep, so I told him without saying a word that I was getting ready to go. I kept looking at the money in the Bible, and then I left.

I saw a very pretty lady with beautiful legs walk up a long flight of stairs and she was smoking a long cigar.

The group, which consisted of many young and old people, was inside a tall modern building that had many floors; some of the men in the group were very loud, and I didn't like that. So I started to go down the many stairs to the ground floor, where the doors led to outside, but there were some men standing there in fine tailored suits, about four or five, the colors were black, gray, blue, and white. They seemed to be waiting for us, so I avoided going out those doors while they were there. When they had gone, some of the group left the tall modern building while some of the others stayed on the upper floors. Outside, I saw a very tiny girl sitting in the top of a tree; she jumped out of the tree into the hands of an Afro American giant. He threw her back into the tree branch that she had been sitting on; she began to talk in dialect. I seemed to be seeing her close even though she was very tiny. She was dressed in a sport shirt and top with tennis shoes.

There was a big party given. I was staying in a very beautiful hotel with other people who were also invited to the big party. The big party was being held in very large beautiful metropolis city. Everyone was being picked up in my boss's car, but I decided that I was going to walk there. There was some merchandise in many boxes that everyone took to the party.

My oldest brother was playing pool in a small little bar, where he could practice his skill and game. I went to a home I lived in and saw many garbage pails for me to put garbage in. In this neighborhood, there were plenty of fine classic and modern cars parked up. I got into one and started to accelerate; the car started to move very quickly down the road. I saw someone else driving their car at the same time. I tried to slow down but I couldn't, so I turned the car so I wouldn't hit their car. That worked for me.

I saw Myra in a neighborhood driving a huge truck; she looked like she was going to crash, and when she did crash her and the truck went right into a home off the road, the truck turned magically into a large bicycle that almost fell on Myra as she fell to the ground. I ran over to her and asked her if she was all right. I started running along the road and Myra ran right along beside me. She asked me a lot of questions about my running; I told her I would have to train a lot more to catch up with the elite runners I would have to run at least one hundred miles per week, sometimes hard and fast. I notice that she was still keeping up with me as we ran. But soon, I left her behind as I ran longer on the road. I could feel myself running across in front of cars that had to stop for people and the crossing light. I could feel the people look at me as I ran. I enjoyed the feeling of running on an open road; there wasn't much traffic.

I was on the west side of a beautiful city, going to a popular restaurant to get food, and they hadn't finished cooking because they served at twelve o'clock, but then I decided to go to another restaurant that was ready to serve food. As I left the first restaurant and went to the second one, I saw a whole group of various people, about one hundred outside the restaurant area. I started to move very fast toward them in the air, elevated like sitting in a chair, moving faster and faster. I tried to slow down but couldn't. I didn't want the people to see me moving so fast. Now I had certainly long passed the second restaurant and I was moving above in the air looking at a superfast two-lane highway with cars moving at superfast speeds going in the same direction in two lanes. I was actually moving faster than the traffic below me. I tried to turn around with the use of my mind concentrating on going in the opposite direction; it started to work a little bit, but the flow of the traffic under me was so great that it forced me to go back to the original flow of the two-lane highway. Now finally, I stopped moving and found myself in the south side of the same beautiful city; the people there were very friendly and warm. I talked to an elder there; he greeted me and talked, then I saw him shooting three arrows at a time at a group of young men who were running toward him, trying to get out of the way of being hit by one of the arrows. I found myself in the group of young men running, trying to get out of the way also of being hit by the arrows, so I hid behind a car and saw one arrow stop in midair. It seemed to have an opening in the middle of it that was an eye or a sensor of some sort, then it kept on going. After this strange ordeal was over, I had remembered that the elder had given me a vertical wooden branch that had two small metallic spheres attached to it at the top; somehow, these had come off during the strange ordeal. I found myself inside of a beautiful house that was somehow my home; inside was classical and modern furniture and decoration. Someone knocked on the door. I opened the door. It was a woman whom I knew, and she was interested in me; she had some small unique animal in her hand that I had never seen before, which was walking on the table in the living room. I told the woman I didn't like this because I don't live with animals inside my house. All she wanted was to be with me. I told her she could wait for me in my house because I had to go back to see the elder. Somehow, I trusted this woman. So I kissed her three times on her lips; she felt hard like a skeleton, then I left. I went to the place where I had met the elder but only saw his son. I told his son that I needed his father to fix the stick that he had given me, and also, I wanted to go through the ordeal for myself. His son told me his father was not there and that he only did the ordeal once a month and that he could get the stick fixed while I waited at his house. So I gave him the stick; he put it somewhere and came back to take me to his house. When I went inside, I saw his family eating at the dinner table. I asked him were these his children, about three? He said yes; they were very bright and full of energy. There were many women at the dinner table too, about four. As I looked at one of the walls in the room, there was a picture actually painted on the bare wall; one of the women's faces had disappeared from the wall, but she was still there at the dinner table. The son of the elder took me back to the place where he had my stick repaired and gave it to me.

I was inside a factory, and the men outside were building a new road; from digging so much, they made a lot of dust. There were two dogs outside that I tried to stay away from. I found myself telling the men inside of the factory that I was leaving, but a man closed the door, sealed, and locked it. I asked him to open it to take a lunch break, and I would give him my watch.

I was with my mother; she was talking to me, so I was washing out the bathtub, and I noticed it was colored blue and black. I tried to clean it off but it stayed on and looked like an abstract painting on the inside of the bathtub.

I was in a very old recreation park at night, just taking a nice quiet walk; there were other people playing a certain game on a big field with all green grass.

Even through it was dark, there was light enough to see the color of the park, which was very green, and the people playing and there was also a group of people walking and talking. I went upstairs to a place where you could sit down in the recreation park like a building. I was trying to read a book when a couple, a man and a woman, came in; they were very light skinned. I kept glancing at them. They didn't seem to notice me. They were very studious, as if they were trying to determine or decide something, then a slim older man came out of an office and locked the door back with a key in his hand. He seemed to be the owner or the overseer of the park. His color was whitish grayish brown, and he looked very hard; he said good morning to me and the couple.

I was running up a gradual hill; cars whistled past so close to me, so I ran higher up in the grass and the trees from the road, so they wouldn't hit me. I ran so close to some small trees and bushes that some bumblebees and their leader, a big black bumble, chased me for a long time until I woke up.

The old man told the young man how he would get into the palace, but when he was finished telling his plan, the palace doors opened, and there were three beautiful women dressed in royal garments. They had been listening to him as he told of his plan, so they left and one came back to the palace. An elaborate door with rich decorative motif on it blocked and sealed the entrance. The old man tried to find its weakness, but it had none.

I was flying through the air in my natural body, high over a metropolis city. Another person, a man, was trying to take my award that was in a box full of money, my prize money. I maneuvered up and down, in and out, up and down, dropping suddenly from one high point to a lower point, trying to get away from the man. I even had to break his hold on my arm several times. Finally, I did get away and I bought everyone African clothes, but it seemed that the house where some children lived needed fixing, and some of the royal family was unhappy about that. So I told them I would fix it.

We were in the forest, our family, brothers, sisters, and mother; we came upon a tall twisting gray tree with many gray branches with very green leaves. They were all twirling and twisting to the very top. My mother said it was a special banana tree, but I didn't see any bananas. We journeyed on through the thick green forest and came upon a large modern ruined building; it had frozen appliances in it. I climbed up high in the building and found a place where there were many electric fans; there was a large deep drop-off almost like a steep valley or cliff inside the building. As I balanced myself and looked over the edge, my mother said to be careful, so I said I would. Then one of my brothers found a metallic teapot; he tried to open it up but it wouldn't, so he borrowed my knife to open the teapot. I opened it easily, and it was full of a whitish water, which came out of the teapot by itself. Everyone was quite happy as we came out of the modern ruins. My father said he was proud of me being a great tai chi master. He congratulated me and so did one of my brothers. I wondered what all the fuss was about.

The city or metropolis was very diverse and wanted to find a place for me and my girlfriend to live; she said she would buy the place, so I was taking a bath in a large rectangular tub, which was surrounded with people in a busy shopping center. There were outside cafes, pubs, stores. I liked the energy, but no one watched me bathe, then my girlfriend came by and said, "Let's go." She had my sunglasses with her to give to me; they very dark and oval-rectangular. I didn't put any clothes on; I just wrapped a towel around my waist because she seemed to be in such a hurry. She wanted to get to the place she wanted to buy for us.

Someone had stolen my green bag in the shopping center. I was determined to find it. I went to the college where there was a young man who worked in the lost and found. He had saw me in store and asked me if I was Calvin. He told me to follow him to a place in the college where he showed me my green bag. I opened it and found that book, the *I Ching* or the *Book of Changes*, was missing from my bag; also my ID and some school papers were all gone.

I was doing tai chi and saw some strangers, maybe husband and wife, outside of my condo; they were looking for a place to sleep outside the condo. I thought maybe they had missed their flight at the airport and didn't have any money. I also went to see where they would sleep, then I went back to my condo to do tai chi, and I was in the college cafeteria doing tai chi, then I was in the street doing tai chi where the cars were. I quickly got out of the street with a spinning lotus double kick; to my amazement, it was so balanced that I felt good about it. Then a beautiful young woman, who at one time was a college professor for me although she seemed to have gotten younger and lovelier, called my name and questioned the material I was wearing. There was also another woman with her I didn't know. I went back to the college and saw a friend who had told me that they had found a bag for me to look at. He had no idea that I had found my green bag, but still I didn't tell him because I wanted to see what was in these bags. In one bag, there was a form of newspaper; all the other bags had nothing interesting in them.

The elegant lady tried on several fashionable hats in the room behind the door. The enormous tiger came out to attack the three people, but he was held back by one person who was biting his tail, until it came off; this seemed to stop him.

There was a drummer with a lady; he asked me what I would play for a melody. I verbally sang a meiotic pattern several times with my own voice and also played ticks like drums, dissecting organic substances that look like various insects. The drummer and the lady watch me closely.

I met a famous runner from college days; I shook his hand and asked him if he still ran a lot of miles. He said he just runs short fast sprints. It seemed that a van was going to take me to the airport, and my brother was taking my friend with his bags in his car, and I wondered why we couldn't go together.

My room was 239; as I opened the door, the smell was so terrible, and there, lying in the bathtub, sleeping on her back was a dark beautiful black woman. I wonder how she could withstand the terrible smell. I ran to get my briefcase, which I had left outside on the lawn; when I came back, I went to the same room and saw about a dozen low single beds with sports participants unpacking next to them. I entered the room and went to a bed; they all acknowledge me as one of the greatest athletes, and I felt terrific with self-esteem. But the temperature in the room was unbearable, stuffy, and hot, so everyone in the room turned around a knob on the wall over their bed, then the room got cooler and breezier instantly, but still, I had a supple feeling it was all in my mind. Then I felt the brilliant wonderful sunlight come through some large windows at the end of the room. All of a sudden, the bright light became very dim. I looked closely at the windows, and I could see that there was a man outside of the windows putting something over the windows so that the light would not be so intense. I didn't like that feeling so the man let the light come through, and I was happy again. As I looked down, my running shoes were not there; although I did have a pair on, they were not the ones I was looking for, so I went outside to find my running shoes. But I didn't find them. Then I went to another room that was very a beautiful office-like room; it had many objects in it and a desk. It was for a lady, but she wasn't there.

I was struck in an elevator and was receiving instructions from a voice from somewhere that came into the elevator on how to use certain number combinations to get out. I was very calm, but I didn't get out of the elevator.

I was late for work; in the work place, I went to a room to change my clothes. There were some employees eating food in there. I accidently knocked down all of a male employee's food off a small table he was sitting at. I tried to offer to get him some more food, but he said it was okay. Then I noticed this type of animal on another table in a bowl; it was round like a ball and seemed to have a birdlike sharp beak. The animal had no legs but a shell dome-like covering; it could levitate or fly but had no wings. I tried to hold it down, but I couldn't; it had too much force to rise up. It came up from a blind spot and attached itself to my ear. I couldn't feel that it was there; one of the other employee told me it was there. I got it off my ear; the other employee tried to crush it with a heavy object, and he finally did after several attempts. It turned into a tiny red crystal. There appeared a woman who wanted to buy the food for me to give to the other employee whose table I had knocked down, so I gave her the money, but I gave her too much money, but I think she took too much money from me, then we argued about it. I could really see the money so clearly, so we just let it go.

There was a friend making tea of a blue color on a stove where he heated the water, but the stove was slanted. I wanted him to heat the water on a next stove that was perfectly balanced and new.

I made a call to my brother in the city and asked him if he wanted to hang out for a while in the city; he was at an outside bar, but he seemed like he had to go somewhere, so he turned me on to another place where I met my sister. We ordered dessert; it was a famous type of pie that was made out of cherries. I could smell the butter in the pie; the cherries were very red in a thick paste in a rectangular package. There were people coming in and out placing orders. Then I left there and went to meet my brother in the part of the city that we had been in previously; we were organizing a band to play music.

I went to the university; there were many students and people there. I and some other people were invited to a special party, but I could not find the party. I went on the elevator several times to several floors, talked to various people also who were going to the party, and still didn't get to the party. I went to a place in the kitchen where I had worked before as a dishwasher and a waiter at the university. I asked for the female cook, one of the head cooks, because I wanted to go through the kitchen to the outside to see if the party was somewhere on the outside, so they told me that the female cook does not work there anymore, but another woman opened the door, and I could see all the way through the kitchen to the outside. She asked me why I wanted to go through. I said just like the others are going through and there were other employees going through, so she let me through. As I walked through, I noticed I had a long rectangular white cardboard box in my hands and a man's voice said, "Let the new Calvin Dallas through." There was a brown-skinned man walking parallel to me for a moment, about twenty feet away as if he knew me. When I got outside, I saw a woman exercising briskly, but there was just a lot space on the university campus and every now and then buildings.

We are all sinners, but to think that you would insult my intelligence by talking about God. I have my Bible; I grew up in the church. But sometimes, you might do the wrong thing. The two men went to another table to eat; before that, my sister came in the restaurant and asked, "What was the matter?" I said nothing. When the two men left my table, they invited my sister to eat with them. She did eat with them for a while. Then a person came from the restroom and dropped a lot of merchandise on the floor. It seemed like it was done on purpose as a distraction. As I left, one of the man at the table said to me, "Go to hell," and I said, "Go to heaven." Then I saw a car driving in the street without anybody in it; it seemed as though it was a mini car that belonged to me. It was going off the road to crash, then I saw another car driving fast on the street on the pedestrian side. Parallel to the fast car was a colorful ball moving at a fast speed, going through tunnels, natural or man-made, that were alongside of the sidewalks. But when the fast car stopped, the colorful ball turned into a small human being who seemed to have on some super costume; the small human sprayed the man inside the fast car with something.

I was supposed to go to the party with my men friends and my oldest brother, but I went to the party without them to see for myself who was there. When I got there, someone said, "The king is here," and I said, "I just came to see who is here for a little while, then I am going back." I noticed that there were all ladies there from old church days; some I recognized, but all of them were very short, and the men were very scarce. I accidently kicked one of the ladies slightly as I jumped over something; she started to cry. So I picked her up, she was that small, and hugged her and gave her some affection. As I held her and looked into her eyes, I realized that I knew her from a long time ago; I asked her, "Do you remember me?" I knew that she remembered me, so she stopped crying. I said, "It's been a long time."

I kept passing my cousin; she ran very swiftly, but I still passed her on a seemingly long coiling silk cloth sheet that went for miles and miles, coiling in circles vertically. Again, she passed me, running even faster, then I would eventually pass her again, then she would pass me again, and this kept going on and on.

I was showing a small group, two men and two women, tai chi attack and defense moves based on the energy of water splashing out and a small circular movement. One of the men, no matter what I did, was not paying attention, so I ran close to him. I made the movements in splashing water attack, with small circles and ball-like circles, and asked him if he felt the energy. I knew he felt the energy even before I did it.

The man had given me several hundred dollar bills to buy a new mouthpiece; he didn't want me to play on his mouthpiece for his trumpet. I found myself with a young beautiful woman rather full, holding her in my arms. I could see she was well developed, and she said to me, "How am I for a woman?" after I started hugging her. I looked at her, and she was smiling at me.

I was in a place, buildings, courtyard, where there were thousands of people, who wanted me to teach them tai chi; I said we only have enough room to show you circle tai chi. I never got to show them; it was just too crowded. I was at a place where my associate and I were staying; the lady of the house was burning various incenses for us, and they had great smells. She looked like a man with red lips and makeup. Her voice was like a lady's, her body except for her face was like a lady, and her legs were great. Then I noticed that there were other ladies there. I spoke to one that was very beautiful. I asked her what her name was. She told me softly, but she went over to my associate; she was more interested in him. A beautiful lady, redheaded, dressed in a soft white tightfitting dress, that showed all her curving parts, bumped into me. I held her gently with one arm for a long time. We communicated with our minds; she was very happy that I was holding her. I could feel her softness go into my body. There was another woman who walked by us and wanted me to stop holding the redhead who just wanted to be with me. So I finally left her and went for a run. I was running through a big city when I asked myself, "Why are you running away from such a beautiful woman?" So I started to run back to the place where she was. I was trying to pass some people on a special highway; they moved very fast in some type of wheel device and I couldn't pass them. I kept running very fast next to them. I kept seeing the highway underneath me, divided. I ran on another lane very fast; the next moment, I was on a bus. In the seat behind me, there were two men and a woman. They tried to get me to spray myself with a certain spray, but I didn't do it. They knew me and called me by my name. The bus had come to a stop because workmen were busy doing some massive type of construction and operations that blocked the section of the street that we had to pass. For me, all I wanted was to get back to the place where the beautiful redhead was. There was an audio announcement inside the bus that seemed to come from a source outside of the bus. There was a fifteen- to forty-five-minute delay, so I got out of the bus through a window, then I started to run back to a street vendor. A beautiful brown woman said to me, "If you're not famous now, I don't know what famous is."

It seemed as though I knew this woman; she seemed very loving and warm. I told her that I had a long way to go, and then I looked at my feet and noticed that I had sandals on my feet. I thought I must have left my running shoes on the bus. Also, I noticed a glass in my hand, a flat 2-D glass with a cellphone-like object that had a small blue triangle on it. I also saw a blue turquoise small pyramid lying next to the cellphone that was on the flat piece of glass in my hands. I stepped into a horizontal section of water, like a small narrow lake, and then the small blue turquoise pyramid fell into the water. Now I was standing in water over my knees. With confidence, I put my hand into the water and retrieved the pyramid back onto the glass, but I noticed that there was something under the blue turquoise pyramid, so I lifted it up and I saw three small wormlike insect creatures. They attached themselves to a string instrument that was very dark, long, and skinny. I was looking at them with two other ladies who had come into the water. One was holding the instrument with the organisms close to her face. She would not let the instrument go. I was worried that they might crawl on her. There was a man watching us, who had fell out laughing at me. The organisms seemed to grow in length vertically.

Of course, she was a beautiful sexy lady; the other woman came in trying to say she was no good, but that wasn't really the case. The other woman was jealous. After the poisonous fluorescent gases were released, I carried the jealous woman up the stairs. I put her on a bed where she could repair and recuperate. The other men and women in the room where the poisonous fluorescent gas was released got out safely.

We rode the horses so gracefully, up and down the green hills, and through the blue sky, with great leaps that seemed impossible, but without fear and acceptance of the mind, it was possible. I could feel the horses' head and see the horses' champion intent to move no matter what. It was simply amazing; we went up the last hill in a majestic super gallop. At the top of this hill, there was a thousand feet straight drop-off to the bottom, so the horses jumped over into the drop-off and floated softly down to the bottom like a feather. We found some warriors there still alive but with no weapons; they were from all nations.

I practiced kung fu with a young kung fu artist who was a lot better than me; he practiced the claw and snake-style kung fu. His strikes were very gripping and piercing, but my breathing technique, fast and relaxing, caused me to reduce the tension of his iron grip and counter his piercing, with swift and soft hitting to vital point spots on his body. I breathed internally.

After the car accident occurred, I went out on the porch and saw a woman crying, then the people who had cause the accident left in their car. My father arrived on the scene as a police to comfort and solve the matter. He also had a son who was white; I told him that he was my brother, even though I was black.

I had dived into the water to see deep-blue water, I could see various fishes and was very deep in vegetation; part of the water I could see many fish there, but I was looking for a flat circular white fish. When I saw it, I speared it with my spear. Then I came out of the water to put the fish in a special place. I saw someone prepare a fire to cook the fish on, but I never saw the fish cooked. I saw a beautiful black young woman with very little wrapped clothes on, but most of her body was exposed similar to an African bush woman living in a jungle or desert and grasslands. She was very pretty, her hair was pulled back but natural; she was inserting small tiny needles into the inside of the middle of both of her arms On a little black painted square that seemed to be horizontally in her skin. She put one in her head, then I saw two young African men get up from a sitting position and go into a push-up position on the floor of an outdoor-indoor tent house on both sides of a man. As the two young men lowered their selves into the push-up position, the man in between lifted a white sheet and pulled a rope; you could see the shadow of the rope through the white sheet, then there was a scream. Next came a loud voice that said, "It's a boy."

I was in the shopping center looking for a special green tea; when I found it, I went to a friend's house who's a runner. He always sets up road races for children and adults; he took most of the tea for himself and left me with only one bag, I went back to the store, but I had to get back to the school to teach. I was just taking a couple days off, and I had told the school secretary that I would be back this very day. When I was with my friend, I asked him the time; he told me, and so I knew I would not make it, so I just hung around in the city.

I was leaving a house where there were three pit bulls with some people; as I left and closed the door, one of the little or smallest ones popped out and fell into my hands. It was small like a round ball, then it grew a little larger than a pup. It latched on to my hand with its teeth. I tried to shake it loose, but the little dog would not let go of my hand in its mouth. There was no pain or blood. On my part, I tried to ask the people in the city; some older gentleman sitting in the city advised me to go to a certain person, who could get me loose. But I didn't have the time, so I took the dog back to the same place where I had first seen it and put it inside the same building; that's when the dog loosed my hand and I closed the door.

I was paying a man money to ride a train that my friend had got on before me, and I was finally let on the train. The train had motorcycles for seats with a pole; the train had no walls, it was open, and you could stand and hold on to the pole or sit on the motorcycle. A dark-skinned man jumped into the train from the ground. I quickly moved over so that he could have my seat, but then, I wondered why I moved over so quickly for him to have my seat.

There was a very good function going on, plenty of people, and visual entertainment of renowned performers that came into the place with a couple of ladies, but it seemed that he was the only one smoking. He seated the ladies by some visual screen with a motion picture on it that other people were watching, but he stood up. I noticed he was the only one smoking; he didn't notice me, but he felt that I wanted to stop him from smoking so he did eventually put his cigarette out, then I noticed that I was lying on a bed watching a video, and there was some kind of patient next to me. The patient sprayed something in my face; I asked him kindly not to do that, but he continued. I got up and saw a nurse. I told her what had happened. We talked for a long time as I followed her. I finally knew that she wasn't going to try to solve this problem, so I told her I was going to file a complaint. She said she would help me; she led me to a place and then told me to follow her, but I didn't. All of a sudden, this male doctor appeared who tried to say that I was someone else. He wanted to keep me in this place; his look on his face was very intense and stern. I thought about showing him my identification; as he rushed toward me forcefully, I walked backward quickly to escape him, as I thought my name is Calvin Dallas and I left that place I could. He wanted to trap me.

My girlfriend and I were trying to connect two cars we were driving with a material; I wanted to use a metal in the racks that hang up clothes. She, my girlfriend, wanted to use cloth. She did take me to all types of clothing stores. Finally, she took me to a place where her friend was the owner; he gave her some cloth to connect the cars. The cloth was very strong; I moved the two cars which were larger than me to a point in a parking lot so that I could connect them with the cloth. The cars were very light, as I moved them both at the same time.

A group of men runners, about fifty and I, ran down the road to get back to our home or section of the city. I ran into the section of town that was prejudiced. People kept getting in my way; one person put out a knife like they were going to use it on me, so I flipped the person over after I took the knife out of his hand. I went back on the road, on my way again.

We traveled down a long country road; the landscape was very green with sufficient trees. The road seemed to go for miles and miles; finally, we reached a place to do laundry. There was a woman in the laundry place who looked at the shirt I was wearing; she read the words on the shirt, and apparently, she had one just like it in the wash. I asked her before she left how far was she going; there were some people making noise, and I could not hear what she said, so I yelled,

"Hey, how far are you going?" She lived just at the end of the road, then I could see how far the road went; it was a winding road.

I was running in a city where I saw two dogs: one was very huge, fat, and overweight; he started to chase me. The other dog was slim and more like a bush dog mixed with pit bull. He also started to chase after me. My fear started me to run from the overweight dog, not realizing that he was too heavy to catch me. But I was thinking to get to higher ground, so I did get to some building and parking lots that were higher than ground level. Then I saw the others coming quickly from the ground level to my level. I told the dog a couple of times to stop and he did. The dog sat down by some people by some steps. He seemed to understand what I was talking about because he listened to me before he stopped and sat down.

I was running to school with a backpack on when I ran past two people who knew me, a young man and a woman. I stopped to talk to them for a while and then I passed them a second time running to school. I got to an enclosed area where I was sure there lived a dog. But a man who lived there assured me there wasn't because he had locked the overweight dog up. As I ran through the enclosed passage, it seemed familiar but still had not got to school. I realized that I had run backward because I was at the beginning of my run to school. I started to run again the same way I started the first time to run to school, but as I looked up the road, I could see the overweight dog sleeping in the pathway so I went another way.

I saw the long metal ladder stretched across the light blue sky to another tropical forest place, but it seemed as though I had climbed that ladder before, so just before I was going to climb the ladder, a person came up to me and started talking to me about something in detail. Then I got off the ladder. There was a guide who I knew was going to take a young lady's life and made like he wanted to help her across the sky ladder. I told her not to go with him because this announcement came through the air that he had been assigned to someone else, but he ignored it and still tried to convince the girl to go with him so that he could eliminate her. I could see it in his face. So once again, I had to get her away from him by calling her intensely. It was as though she was so sound and not listening effectively to me.

I met someone who said they had my order, so I talked to them a while; one person had his leg in my face, so I gently removed it. The other person asked him if he was a musician and he said no.

I was walking home with my head down, then I saw an old friend and I greeted him. I asked him how the missus was? I gave him a handshake; I noticed that he wore black gloves. I met another old friend who seemed to be talking a lot when I asked him how it was going. I told both of them that I was thinking about getting a new trumpet. Then they both ran across the street, as if they both had the same appointment.

I found myself on a bus asking a person about a marathon, and he said it was for adults, not just children, but the ticket I will pay for the entrance fee is called jealousy, so it's only two dollars. I saw the man get on another bus, but the bus ahead opened its windows. I was in a new city.

I went to a beautiful home where I looked at some lovely rooms; I returned to the same home the second time and the rooms were sealed off; there were no more doors, just a wall. So the house looked totally different.

Twice, I was in a car with an older woman who was sitting in front of me facing me and with a stern look, pressing my body; it seemed in a metal way, she was trying to make me ejaculate, but I resisted. The second time, she tried to hold my arm down.

I was in a large stadium where I was teaching female and male students tai chi.

There were some nude women whom wanted to come into my room, but I didn't let them.

I was in a room with an old girlfriend; we laid together, and her energy was warm, penetrating, and divine, and she was holding me very lovingly.

I was in the apartment with my mother; she said that my father was here to give me a present, but I had thought he was dead. I saw him lifting a great huge box up the stairs. It was mostly vertical. I could see he had his hat and glasses on and was kind of skinny and dark. I gave him a hug as I cried a couple of times. I was so glad to see him. But I was kind of shocked because the present he bought me unveiled itself automatically as a huge robotic camera. It was a giant electronic vertical robot, included with it was a drum set. But I was still very happy to see my father.

I was smoking a large cigar in the company of my brother. Then he went and brought back many students to look at my art show. I had done many paintings. One of the young male students who was walking with a cane because he had hurt himself asked me a question, "Should a person go looking for a mate or let the mate find him?" I said the mate should find him. The young student was very irritated with my answer because his face had an angry expression on it.

I was in a room where I taught children art, but I was putting up a large piece of artwork that covered the whole wall and the person that was helping me was talking about some type of group that he was involved creatively with. There were children outside on the field taking beautiful pictures in lovely colored dresses and suits; it seemed as though they were graduating. I was trying to get a group of students that I could teach art at the same time this was happening.

I was talking to my mother; she was lying in bed, but she had such a beautiful young face and body. I was telling her that she should go to Chicago to enjoy herself more. I felt that she was very sexy.

I was with a beautiful woman; she was building her self-esteem by showing all her various body poses that she could hold. I was talking and watching her closely. I wanted to kiss her, but I didn't. She was very sexy.

My brother was in a glass factory working. I told him he should communicate more quickly and often, and I looked at him straight in his eyes. He looked at me kind of shocked. Then I ran away, trying to keep my tears from coming.

A very large dog started to play with me until I finally got away from the dog; he didn't want to let me go.

I followed a group of my friends into a place where they were going to perform an operation on a group of people; the energy was too much for me.

I took a test in school; an older woman said that I had passed the test, but when I looked on the paper, I saw an F, but she said I had done pretty good.

I was outside in the back of my house doing tai chi movements and singing; everything was so clear, so after a while, I went to the front of the house to sit on the porch, and I noticed the neighborhood looked so sunny and still. I tried to look into the front porch windows into the house, but they were tinted with a dark color.

I was at a school and some workmen didn't let me go into a certain part of the school grounds. I told them that they were rude; I had to teach a certain class of children that day but never made it to the classroom. I was with a very unusual lady. I liked her company but my mother advised me to leave her alone. I told my mother that I am a grown man now, but it didn't matter to her.

I told a gentleman in the store not to harass the young lady; if you like her, tell her directly. Try to go for life.

There was a lady who was beating another girl with some type of object. I saw her do it, then I went and took the object from her and I kept pointing it at her, saying to her that God would make a way for her somehow and I told her I am her elder. She was very large and rough; she made an attitude to listen.

I was walking in a city on one side of a long fence that separated the sidewalk from the parking lot. I saw a young woman who was kind of intoxicated with liquor; she seemed to be a little bit angry, so she started to throw rocks at me. I ducked out of the way; she missed most of the time. Finally, I told her she was going to have to pay for this. She came over to my side of the fence. I had reach behind my back and into my pants to make like I had a gun; she also reached into her pocket and came out with a knife. I threw her on the ground.

I was trying to get a dollar from the money, five, tens, twenty dollar bills I had in my hand to pay the bus driver, so I could put it into the box. A man on the bus tried to take the dollar from my hand to put in the box. I told him to cool out. But he didn't; even when I put the dollar in the box, the man pushed the dollar farther down into the box with his figure. The bus driver was telling a story to someone on the bus in a very intense way. I could see his face; it looked so familiar, like I knew him from the past. Before I got on the bus, I was walking down a sidewalk, and some young girls were throwing snow at each other in front of me, but I had come from walking through a house that I lived in, seeing a woman who I knew and a man who was in bed but not asleep. I said something to the man as I walked out of the house.

I was taking a shower in an abandoned cellar. I had dried off, and I noticed a figure of a bald man standing under one of the archway in the cellar; he looked like a statue at first, then I shot my towels at him that I had dried off with after my shower, then he laughed and started to talk and move. To me, if seemed like a ghost or trick, people young and old started to come from everywhere in the cellar; they basically asked me if it was okay for them to eat the food that I had there for myself to eat. I said sure; one lady asked if I would get a lawyer, I said no. I never had seen these people before.

I was in an aikido dojo where the sensei was telling me and showing me to keep moving and threw me with a hand technique; I did a semi-break fall that was very soft.

I tasted the milk in the glass that the other customer in the restaurant had given to me; he said it didn't taste right, so I asked him if I could taste it and he said yes. He gave it to me when I ranked the milk and tasted it, I spit it out so quickly, like an explosion, because it was so sour.

I saw myself with a lot of hair, washing it with a substance that made it grow long, soft, and black instantaneously. I really had a lot of hair; I washed and rinse it out in a bathroom where there was lots of water.

I kept on using someone's bathroom in a large apartment building; it seemed as if no one was there. I just had to pee, but I noticed each time I used the bathroom, I saw a lot of water on the floor and clothes on top of the water to dry up the water. So I felt there was a leak of some sort.

I was painting a monumental landscape of a city area; three gentlemen watched me closely as I painted.

One of them painted a stylistic landscape while I painted. When he showed it to me, it was very small, but I told him it reminds me of the city of Paris in France. After I had finished painting, the men took my painting to another level in the lower part of the building to study it, then they brought it back up to me; it seemed that I had painted on a monumental-sized rug. One of the men had asked me if I had studied in Saint John; I said I studied at the University of Wisconsin in Madison.

I was the owner of some land that a certain individual, who seemed to have large veins that protruded from his skin like rivers, was trying to overcome me, but I accepted his challenge because I knew he could not overcome me.

I saw an extensive program on color in a teacher's classroom; he let us look at some pictures that were about one hundred landscapes.

I helped a man to get on a subway train; the man had no clothes on, but when we got off the train, we were still underneath the ground.

I was eating dinner with my friend's girlfriend; he saw me and went to another table to eat with someone else, and it was as it was supposed to be.

I went shopping in a big supermarket, and I was just interested in buying the apple juice; most of the saleswomen were selling different containers of apple juice.

I was going to run a second workout, but a beautiful lady picked me up and gave me a ride to her house; she offered me bread of various textures. I chose the thick type; she said she was going to change her clothes and bathe while I ate. When she came back, she looked great. I tried to drink some water, but there was no place except for the ceiling that the water was coming out from. She said she had to let someone in, but when she let the someone in the house, it was a large Doberman pincher. She said it was something else, but I could clearly see it was a Doberman pincher because I saw its pointy ears. She let it into another room; it went in quietly.

I was in the city and saw a lovely lady and said good morning, then I noticed she was going to get a Doberman pincher to walk with her; she seemed to be very happy, but while I was trying to avoid her, I ran into another lady who also bumped into me. I said sorry but she kept on walking in another direction. She was right behind me, then I said I don't like pit bulls that almost look like a pig running toward me. The dog tried to bite my leg and foot, but I jumped up high several times to evade this pit bull, but finally, he got a hold of my leg, but I shook him off. He still came back to bite me again. I could feel his teeth; they didn't hurt, but the dog was very aggressive.

I was looking for a lady who was a great friend of mine. I saw a man in his home dancing; he came to his door when he saw me and said he knew where the party was that lady was having fun and that for me to wait in a room, he would be back to show me. He gave me a checkered shirt and left me in this room. I heard dogs growling on one side of the room behind the wall, but I couldn't get out. I tried to open the door, but it wouldn't open. I kept on hearing the growls.

I was attacked in the head by a flying bird of prey; it latched on to the top side of my head and buried its claws and beak deep into my head. I saw myself go unconscious for a long while until some man came and got the bird off my head. I could actually see myself, blood all over my head and body. I felt as if there were holes in my head, and I wanted to take a shower to stop the bleeding, but I didn't.

I was walking in the city when a car pulled up in front of me and the side door opened up slowly; a black man was in the front driver seat and a black woman sat in the back seat. They asked me if I wanted a ride, so I got into the car. I held the hand of the black woman and the man who was driving the car and had a good feeling that almost made me cry. I had a feeling that they knew me very well.

I walked down some basement steps and heard people crying and yelling for mercy shrilly; somehow, my father went down the stairs with me, and so I found a young baby who I carried in my arms. Back up the stairs, the cries and shrills for mercy were all gone.

I was at a house where one lady was taking a shower. I went into another room where a tall beautiful lady grabbed me into her arms and pulled me close to her face and said that I belonged to her. I tried to kiss her everywhere, but she limited my progress. I kept wondering when we were going to make love, but we never did. I found myself wearing a strange glove that was black and had a place for figures at my head.

I was sitting down at a bar restaurant, talking to my mother about relationships; I also was talking to a lovely lady.

A man came to my condo and asked if his wife could live in my condo while she was going to have a baby. I wondered where I would live because it seemed like a great honor, but the man said she had done it before.

Then I looked into my condo and saw that there were two unidentified people, a man and a woman, who were walking slowly through my condo, talking calmly to each other. They didn't seem to see me, and it seemed like there were no walls in my condo. All condos seemed to have merged into one.

I was at a dinner with relatives and noticed that someone had taken some of my food out of my plate, but I still ignored it and continued to socialize with good cheer.

I was in a building in a large room with many people, who were sitting down in a nightclub atmosphere; there was a gentleman who made supple eye contact with me. I felt like he knew me, but I didn't go to meet him, but instead, I went outside to see a set of unfamiliar faces in the city landscapes.

All Laundromats in the city had closed because they had run out of water. Everyone was standing outside the Laundromats with unwashed clothes.

I was in a large room getting ready to practice tai chi; I noticed it had two sections.

I was in a large beautiful house. I asked my mother, "Where are all the kids?" She said that they had all. I felt something, a quiet hush. I looked outside and saw a lot of kids running up and down the place with kittens. They heard me coming down the steps, and they started running this into the house. I told all of them to sit down; they were all sizes and colors. I told them that they just couldn't come into this house running, so they all sat quietly.

I was in a college setting, looking for my room, with many new faces.

I was in a room with a group of people, men and women; we were just laughing, and we felt good. We were talking and just laughing and looking at each other.

I signed a document for land and a house; the names that supported me on the document were A and B.

People were eating people, and then the eaters would change into geometric rubbery forms. I tried to get Mr. T to help as a good friend, but he wouldn't move, so quite a few people were consumed.

I was holding a box full of money; there were other men with a small rectangular metal box, full of money. You couldn't take the money. I gave the box to a man at a table, and he looked at me for a long time. Then out of many needles, he picked up a needle. I looked at him without fear for a long time, then he picked up the box and left, and I picked up the needle from the table that the box was on and left.

I was driving around in a white car, then I went to a house to live and some people were already in the same house; they asked me to sleep in a certain place. I told them it was okay. I would use the floor, then I went outside and started up a different car. I thought it was white, but I noticed the color was a dark color when I had got out of the car. I actually turned the key in the car to start it, then I got out the street, and the town seemed to be empty and very quiet.

I was riding in the front seat of a car, with a band member who was driving. I could see into the other car that was across from us; the two people sitting in front I knew, one was a former tai chi student of mine and now was an instructor in jujitsu. The other person was also someone I knew but not that well. I didn't try to look directly at them, but the person who was driving the other car stopped, got out of the car, and came over to talk to me, and then he got back in his car and drove off. I still notice that I didn't try to look at them directly, even though I could see them very clearly. We drove both cars to a destination where there was a big musical party. When they got out of the cars and went up to the front doors, they open the doors and told us to sit down outside, so we did sit on the concrete. The one man who I had taught tai chi came over and gave me a handshake and then, inside the house, gave us some cooked golden bread that was shaped like swirls in white plates.

I was in a family house where I went to sleep, then in the morning one of the brothers came into the house to wake me up. I got up and organized my room. I noticed that I told the brother I had great dreams. I was looking for a small gold square metal object that helped me dream. The mother of the family kept checking on me; she was my mother too. At one point, she looked in on the room at me, and I just had my underwear on; as she looked at me as my mother, I realized how old I was. She saw me as her son, who she gave birth to; that was respect enough for her. As I finished cleaning my room, I noticed that they prepared several dishes of food for us to eat.

The lady was flying in through the air trying to attack us, me and my friend, with a wooden object, so we trapped her by getting her to land on the ground after destroying the wooden object. I held the lady down and I asked her if her name was Karen several times. She seemed to be very nervous and frantic; she was white and shaking. From somewhere, she grabbed a human female face mask and put it on her face. Now she looked totally different, but she was still a nervous wreck.

I was in a place that I had been before, and there were dogs I was trying to escape from. This time, the dogs wanted to attack me but were held back by beautiful women. I was very grateful.

I saw a very sad worried old lady, then suddenly her facial expression changed to one of happiness and youthfulness, so I went over to her and she asked me if I would like to make purchases in her business or become a partner; the next moment, I was attacked by a group of women who were nothing more than skeletons covered with dark-colored clothes. They attacked me one by one slowly. I used slow kung fu movements to counter their attacks, I could actually see the bones through their clothes. The happy lady looked on closely at my ordeal; one of the skeleton women actually attached herself to me and tried to drain my energy, but instead, I drained hers.

I was disciplining or talking to a little girl who was not listening; finally, I told the little girl to go to her place, and then I sat down in the church and listen to some musicians playing music in the church. One played cello, the other guitar, and one played the saxophone. There was also a lady singing, the music was so light and soft, the lyrics were "True love will come, the world will be one." As I sat there; tears almost came to my eyes. I had to wipe my eyes off with my hands.

As I looked around the church, there were not that many people there, but I felt like leaving, but I stayed.

I gave a big lecture on shape to a class of students and gave the example of purpose with construction workers who are very strong and every shape they used had a purpose.

My mother was telling the people who are going to the musical event not to forget me, but I told her just for her own benefit after seeing that there was only rice to eat that was cooked on the stove that they were jealous of me, then I saw some people come into our big store which also was our house. My young sister, cousin, and my mother started to curse one lady bad, but then they saw that I was looking at her, and they stopped.

I was in the family house and my oldest brother was upstairs with a beautiful lady. I wanted to brush my teeth, but someone was always in the downstairs bathroom. So I went upstairs and saw the lady and my brother nude together, but he was working at his desk on some type of project. I finally did brush my teeth in the bathroom upstairs, and when I came out, my little sisters and brothers were in the room with the lady, but now she had clothes on. I told them to go back downstairs and they did.

I was in a beautiful decorated traditional martial arts dojo practicing tai chi with a traditional tai chi master and students; after the class, he took me in another room and asked if we should get a larger place for the tai chi practice, and I said yes. He started to take down all the traditional decorations for the dojo. One of the tai chi students needed some help with her luggage; she said it would be better for my back if I rolled the luggage on the floor because it was quite heavy, so I did and I found that it was light, but when I got outside and rolled the luggage on the street, it was quite heavy.

I was in a theater watching some women dancers get ready for a show; their costumes were dazzling and sparkling.

My brother said he wanted to teach people the art of sexual kung fu, and I said, "Let me give you a suggestion. Do it in private."

I was in a house waiting to get a bus but had missed a couple of buses already, then finally, I saw one bus waiting for people to get on at the bus stop. I ran from the house that I was in across the street with some light luggage and got on the bus to meet three suited men, who wanted to see my identification documents, so I pulled out my wallet, and before I found them, one of the men took my wallet from me and found my photo ID. He held it up so I could look at it closely. Yes, it was wearing African clothes, so he let me enter into the bus. The other men in suits seemed to be jealous of him because they started to talk in riddles.

My whole body disappeared as I finished writing on the paper and read it. I was gone; I had vanished.

The married couple next door, I heard them talking to their friend. As I walked, I thought of my large almost gym-like house; it was so spacious for exercise. I looked outside my door, and there were two large low tables. I carried them into my place and the table seemed to become larger. I tried it out for a bed; it seemed to be okay. But I wondered why my neighbors gave me these tables without asking me if I wanted them.

I was really playing my trumpet and experimenting with patterns and harmonies of musical variations, and a lady came into the room; she started talking about saliva. I showed that I controlled that with the valves on my trumpet. I even let some of the saliva out of the trumpet so she could see.

We were given special notebooks for teachers; only then, we were given our female guide to a large university campus cafeteria to eat. I couldn't decide whether to go to the bathroom or eat; they had comfortable lounge chairs to sit down and eat at. I tried to read the sign above the doors; they had a strange word on them, not men or women. When we had got our food and sat down, I noticed that all of us had a little salad dressing.

A lady gave me an electronic device to make my skateboard go faster and it actually got me on the highway. I had to be careful because the cars and trucks were going in the opposite direction. One car almost hit me, but I jumped off my skateboard to avoid it. I shouted loudly at the people in the car with curse words. After that, I became worried that they would stop the car and start trouble with me, so I kept my eye on them. When they did stop farther up the road, I started to run quickly. I ran into beautiful dirt alleyway that had lovely green gardens and lush homes. Then I found myself running toward our family home in the snow with no top on, but long pants and black high-heeled snow boots on. I could see from a distance a huge sea cargo ship next to our house in the front, out parked in the street; my mother and sister were waving to me with their hand and arms. I waved back as I ran closer. I could see my brother there just looking at me but nothing else.

I was trying to get away from a lady who knew me, a beautiful blonde; she was chasing me and gave my presence away to another woman. I jumped across a street miraculously in front of several moving cars that seemed to slow down when I jumped, and I landed in a person's yard who asked me why did I do something to his dog. He said he was going to get his dog, so I started to run again.

I went into a store to buy some soup and toothpaste; when I got to the checkout counter, the young lady who was very large came over. I asked her how much was the soap; she told me and left me there with other people without any service.

I went into a restaurant and a young lady came over to me and politely took my order from me, then another young lady brought me my food so graciously; she was very pleasant and polite. I asked her if she had any mustard; at first she didn't reply, then she said yes. Then after she left, a man came over to my table and started pointing with his hand over my food. I tried to move his hand away, but he kept on doing it. So I told him I was going to complain to the manager, and what he was doing was against the law. The man looked at me in shock.

I was trying to register for my final year in a university and a beautiful young lady helped me register; after that, we sat and talked about ourselves, then her people drove up in a car. They were happy to see her. She became very small as she got into the car.

I was watching a woman burn a fish in the water with a certain type of rock. Then she asked me to take the fish out of the water with certain tools. I did ask her would it bite me, and she said no. The fish grew tremendously when I took it out of the water. It became the white and rectangular. The other man and I took the fish outside the university campus. It was snowing because I could see the large snowflakes, and the grass was white. I slid down a slippery small hill with the fish in my hands. We were taking the fish to the river.

I woke up and saw that my father was on the coach sleeping; he woke up, and he had a suit on. He seemed to be saying something, but I could not hear it clearly. Then I went outside for a run. When I came back, there were thousands of small black rats running from my bedroom. Everyone was watching them; it seemed to be no end to them. I told my oldest sister to give me my pants and shirt, which had some money in them, and she did. She went into the room where the rats seemed to be multiplying to get my pants. There was a woman talking to me about the rats; we don't know why they are there. I told her that she was talking with some humor in her voice; when she looked straight into my eye, I let her know that I was not responsible for the rats.

I woke up in a dream. I got to the bathroom; as I went in, I noticed that my father had woken up too, but I went in before him, then another person told me to take it easy on the water because it was low, then my father came into the bathroom and started to wash his face as I brushed my teeth.

I was talking to a man and his girlfriend, telling him that being a photographer was different from being a politician.

I was in a large bedroom where many men were going to sleep for the night; my brother owned the room. He fell on a bed that was not set up right and had broken down when he slept on it.

I was in a factory putting up and organizing products in a container when a group of children and parents came in; the manager told them to get out. I noticed some of the containers were shaped like musical instruments.

A person was holding a dog, a guard dog. I looked at the dog; he was trying to get to me. At first, I could see his bear mouth; the next time I looked at him, he had a morsel on his mouth. The next time I looked at him, he had a mussel on.

I was walking in a tropical area with beautiful beaches and houses with green palm trees beside them in the hills. I could hear the Rasta talking. I took off my clothes, except for the underwear, and had decided to take a swim; as I enjoyed the view and the beautiful walk, I felt great, then I saw some men playing some sort of game, where they were hitting a white ball. The ball went way up in the air and dropped not too far in front of me; another ball went higher in the air, and before it could hit the ground close to me, a dark man came running quickly over to me and caught the ball in his hand and said to me, "This ball is for you."

I was in my father's house, helping him wash the dishes.

I woke up in a place that was very rough and harsh. I was wearing rugged clothes, and I had white gloves on my hands. I looked outside of some jagged window that was broken, and it seemed the atmosphere was like that of thunder and lighting. But then I started to dance and I heard a voice, saying that this was a dream. But I felt it was so real. I didn't try to change anything in the dream; I just really hoped that I would wake up.

As I walked on the fertile green hill, I could see green for a long way. I felt happy that everywhere I looked on top of the hill was green. The thought of what the woman who at the time, I was in the classroom with, other people said only did seven lesson plans for the school year. You did not write the first part to the lesson plans. I told her she was not supposed to be saying that to me in front of the students. I told her, "Don't underestimate me because I have already written a book and other great feats and plan for the future."

The woman came over to me, wanting to make love to me, even though I was with another woman. So a man shot a lightning bolt out of his body through his hands to the woman's body, and her body opened up to see wires inside of her; she was a robot.

The runners ran exceptionally fast through the housing complex; in fact, I thought it was too fast, so I went to talk to my college coach; he was in his office. He asked me was I ready to take a hiking trip in nature. I said I didn't want to see any bears or other wild animals on camping out; he explained to me that it would be safe, but he had a leg that was bothering him.

It was late in the night or about 8:00. I ran to the school, and I stood outside the schoolroom window talking to a teacher; she was working late. She was going to change, so she went to the lady's room. I went to the men's room; I saw that children were coming into the school at that late hour.

She had baked various breads at the restaurant. I had ordered raisin bread.

I was at an Indian home where many married couples stayed but had no children there. One of the wives was in the kitchen, and she was eating breakfast; her husband had left. I hoped that she would give me something to eat, but she didn't. I put on some clothes on; I had just woken up. I had some very light-blue jeans on. Before that, I had drunk some very tasty juice, and then I looked into a rectangular container that was filled with different juices and other products.

I ran the second time around the same path, through the rural neighborhood, but this time around, it seemed longer and higher; in fact, as I looked up the road, it seemed so high and long that I stepped and fell. I stopped going up the road.

I had to go another place in the country and stay at a white couple's renting house. When I went out on the town, I met a gentleman who gave me a key to unlock his business at five a.m. I was at some type of gathering of people; I convinced him that I could do it because I was staying right next to his place of business. All I had to do was to unlock the gate that protected his facility. I went back to my rental room, and as I stood there to unlock the door, I quickly turned around and bumped lightly into a lady's stomach who was standing behind me so closely and she had been watching me all the time. I apologized for hitting her and began talking to her. Her boyfriend came out with an attitude and wanted to fight me. Then all of sudden, out of nowhere, a young lovely black woman came out of nowhere; she pretended to be my woman or lover. She said, "Let's go home." So we went to her grandmother's rent-a-room place; when we got there, I looked at the room and saw that it was hidden with a large curtain. I moved the curtain back and saw the other couple coming our way with the jealous boyfriend, so we hid ourselves and watched them walk by. We went to a party and the same couple was there. I showed the jealous boyfriend some simple kung fu moves; he liked that very much. But the woman who pretended to be my lover really liked me a lot; she wanted me to be close to her and smell her lips. Her boyfriend now tried to chill a bottle of red wine by wrapping it with a towel with ice inside of it, around it, and putting it into a boiling solution. When he unraveled it, the experiment didn't work. I was a bit confused and asked them had they ever unlocked the gate, and they said yes.

I saw many men work next to the curb of the road; they seemed to be in a ditch, almost up to their heads. They were pulling some type of cable rope together. I ran past them several times, trying to cross the street to catch the bus. We, my father and I, drove in a strange subway train-like vehicle on a strange track that didn't have steel in it, but geometrical convex surface patterns made of stone or earth. We went through a tunnel for a while, then the vehicle stopped, and we got out and went to the surface. We saw a strange giant creature; the creature said something about guns, and it looked a little human like. We also saw another creature that looked like a mole or badger; it seemed to move at a moderate pace. It had four legs and was huge. We tried to hide in some old abandoned houses that were once part of a thriving city because we thought that the creatures were after us. But they never did come after us or catch us.

I went to a house where there was a babysitter; she seemed to be fifty years old and she was watching my brothers. They were all doing different activities. She knew me, but there was one brother that was not in the room. I wanted to see him, but I just visited with my other brothers. I had just taken a long shower before I came to see them.

There were many children and adults in the newly made-over building with many rooms; it seemed to be some type of school. I knew some of the teachers and students. We rode a bus to leave the school. There were thousands of people.

I was on stage with several bagua and tai chi masters; we were doing various moves with circular movements and repetition, and we were actually giving a live performance in demonstration mode.

I was in a room by myself, trying to sleep, but I heard some people walking around upstairs, talking, so I was very uncomfortable trying to sleep because it seemed that something invisible was in the room with me.

I was telling a person who I never forgave because he had beaten up a lady in front of me how great my adventure was of coming to Florida; a friend was driving me all the way to Las Vegas. I told him the first hotel we stopped to check out was second class, but the second was first class, top of the line. I told him that the people there were fantastic because I was talking to him from a party in a hotel on a phone. I told him that the swimming pool was great. He had very little to say. I realized that I had finally forgiven him, but he had some remorse because he hung up the phone because he thought that I said good night. There was a long silence after I talked to him. I asked him what was he doing tonight, but he thought I said good night.

On a secret mission, we dressed in black and went to a place of business that was closed down to acquire a certain item that was very important; we got back of the business and confiscated certain files and there were a couple of people in the front, but we got out before they found out what was being done.

I took a great camera, very large, and put it together, and then I snapped a picture of women in a shopping center.

I asked the people who looked like Mexicans and Indians if this was the hood. They laughed and said, "You're not far from the hood, it's just over there." They brought me a large fat smoke stick of Marianna that I didn't want to smoke. I told them that I wanted to keep my head clear, so I did take some of their drink. But it looked like there was some type of seeds with living organisms in it. After we drank it, the others and I started pulling sticky glue-like substances out of our mouths.

The professor wanted to take me to his class; when I got there, the class looked brand-new or remodeled. The professor said that they remodeled the class every two months.

Some little girls gave me some heavy color balls that they had made, but I dropped them on a crowd of people, who were sitting on some bleachers, but no one got hurt; I was at a festival-like event.

I was in a city where the light would get brighter in a second and everybody would move to other levels with people in them in downward vertical spiral movement. It was not necessarily in the ground but in some type of space.

I was running in a park that was very green and small; they were playing romantic tunes of a famous soul singer.

I had got married in my dream and was helping my wife move some furniture, but as I looked at her, I wished that I would have waited and married someone more beautiful.

I was led through the dark by a lady's hand pushing me to a place that was still dark, but now I could see this lovely light-skinned woman who was very young and so we danced closely and slowly together. She began to cry when I told her I was looking for my brother; she said she wanted me to buy her some chicken to eat.

The men continued to attack me with various knives; every time, I defeated him, but he never seemed to die.

I visited my father in the family house; he was close by my side.

In my mind, I was terrorized by my own fear in the dream; someone came into my room to help me. I was screaming in my mind.

I jumped up and caught the see-through cylinder plastic container that had several tiny crystals in it. The container floated in the air, a couple of feet horizontally above my head. I met the lady who told me her arm and hand was hurting her; I walked with her and held her hand. I asked her if she ate pork because her hand seemed to be swollen, and she said yes. I told her not to eat pork anymore. Her friend came and surrounded her with hugs.

As I walked to the main building, I heard a type of vibration music that seemed to be like a music score for a motion picture in which I was the main character. I went up the steps to go inside the building, and there were guards, adults, and their children; they did not seem to notice me, and the music had stopped. I was viewing a magnificent film from the beginning to the end, with soldiers, generals, captains, dressed in oriental uniforms that seemed to be communist but, at the same time, merged with the Caribbean Islands culture. At the end of the film, I saw oriental lettering for the credits. After seeing the film, I met several times a lovely light-skinned lady; she said nothing to me but smiled at me.

I went down on an elevator; when the door opened, I walked out unto a little passageway and saw another door. All kinds of people of color were trapped behind the doors because their hands were sticking out of the edges of the door and the door was not completely closed.

I was in an area where there were plenty of soldiers and guest people. I was walking through the crowd trying to avoid the soldiers, when I saw one officer rudely yell at an officer for something he did. As I continued to walk through the crowd, I heard a blasting sound in the air; as I looked up, a missile had been shot off. I could see that it was very large, and it was heading for a vehicle as a target a half a mile away. When it hit the target, it also exploded some type of building. I could see some of the parts of the explosion come down on some of the people who seemed to be watching the event; they were smashed.

I was in a place where there were many scholarly young beautiful women who were discussing their concepts on science and life in the universe. Then we all had large separate bowls of cooked rice. I ate so much rice that someone came to me to remix the rice so that I had to wait to eat again.

As the beautiful brown-skinned young lady lay in my arms, I experienced great love and joy. She was smiling all the time, and we were moving through nature's ecosystems, forests with mountains of green. We were moving without any vehicle. I remembered making love to her; she said she was going to get me again.

CALVIN EARL DALLAS

Walking back and forth in the same area in a familiar neighborhood, I realized that I was trapped in a maze-like pattern and I kept walking in circles or rectangle areas.

The famous musician was finished playing the concert. I went to the lounge and put on a large wide-rimmed multicolor hat with a long orange cape. I remembered how the famous musician played the guitar-like violin-looking instrument, plucking the high and low strings at the same time with both hand figures, creating new melodies; he looked at me and said, "Don't forget about saving the gang members," with several rhythm glances.

I was in a house sleeping in a bedroom with my lady friend; she was in one bed and I was in another. All of a sudden, there appeared an older woman in the living room. I was still in the bed; she was standing there looking at me. I was looking at her from my bed. My lady friend got up to help a little boy go to the bathroom and pee. She was short and light-skinned; the older woman came closer to me and asked me did I see where she was standing, and I said yes. Then she told me to get out of the bedroom and go. My lady friend told her no, so the older woman left. I went back to sleep, but there was loud music playing the whole time. I was trying to sleep, then my lady friend looked at me and got up.

I was having a great time partying with these new people; it seemed as though I knew them. We were drinking a lot and having a lot of fun talking to each other. Then when it was time to go, most of the ladies who having the most fun all had masks on. One of them was very drunk; she was having problems with her car. So some other guys who were really driving wiggly asked me if I wanted a ride home and I looked at the way they were driving and said I would walk, but when I started to walk, I could see in a distance familiar vegetation and land; it seemed that there were a lot of people by a massive river. I asked a fellow along the way did I have to cross that river to get home. He said yes. So I saw someone who looked like they were at the party. I waved at him as he drove by. Far down the road, he stopped and I ran to his car. I got in and said thanks. I asked him was he going across the river, and he said yes. The next thing I knew, I was up in the air, traveling very light in a huge type of vehicle that was moving on some type of rail or wire in the sky. I saw this pretty well from the inside of the vehicle. The man offered me a rum drink that he made himself; he poured water into it. I drank some, and it tasted very smooth and like a mellow fruit. He said that he always drinks his with a lot of water. Then he offered me some smoke; he had a large bag of it. The smoke was very green and had buds that looked like a rose. He explained to me how he created the rosebud look. As I continued to talk to him, he was very pleasant and understanding.

I was at a building in a room where a teacher had a group of students listening to his lecture that was about certain elements and contents of China that were measurable and significant. So we were told at the end of the lecture to go and do some research. Two other young ladies and I were walking outside, then we started to glide quickly about seven inches off the ground; it seemed that we glided for a long time. All of a sudden, we floated up into the tree tops and it started to pour rain. I came crashing down suddenly into the ground. I put my blue raincoat on and started to run to catch up with the two ladies. They were way ahead of me. I could see that clearly because the heavy rain made their bodies seem like moving shadows racing across city blocks. They ran to the front of the building; it was still raining a lot. I heard someone call my name, "Dallas," then I saw them standing with the front doors open; it was still raining.

There were two ladies; they were fighting with swords. They stabbed each other with the sword deeply. It seemed that they both immediately died. But they both changed into umbrellas, one I could hear was breathing gently, and the other had no breath. I put the umbrella that was breathing in a safe place. When I saw the husband of that particular breathing umbrella that was a woman before, I grabbed him and told him that his wife had been stabbed by another lady. She was dying. The husband was shocked. I didn't tell him that she had turned into an umbrella.

I saw that I could get to my destination by crossing a long bridge, but when I started to cross the long bridge I started seeing everything upside-down so I stopped walking across the long bridge. I noticed that below the bridge, there were several houses very close to each other. By traveling through those houses, I could also get to my destination, but I got a feeling of being closed in, so I didn't make it to my destination.

I walked up the back stairs of an apartment house; there on the back entrance was my cousin and her husband with their son, eating dinner, and I told them I would go around the other way, but before I left, my mother came around and opened the back door; she wore glasses and opened the back door. She looked very different, happy, and healthy; she was glad I came to dinner. There were lots of people eating at her house.

I was in a neighborhood where a tall man invited me into his house across the street from where I stood; he said to me, "Welcome back." I realized that I had been there before. I took a rest on the bed in his house, then something happened. There was a report that went out in the news that the police were looking for a group of young men. So I left the tall man's house, saying I would return. He thought I was one of the men in the group. I saw my oldest sister who was walking her two little dogs; one of her little dogs jumped up on me and nipped me in the back of the neck. I knocked him off me quickly. I told her if she could not control them, I would create a weapon to protect myself. I created a long pole with a curve blade at the end of it. My oldest sister put a cover over the curved blade. We traveled to another house where my sister locked the dog in a certain area and I had my own room.

I found myself in a large dark living room with a medium-dark smooth heavyset woman who was burning incense and praying; at one point, she lay down in her bed, then she got up and continued to pray. She asked me if I could feel them and I said yes, they are all here, the spirits. At that point without any effort on my part, my whole body started moving very fast in a circular pattern while standing up around the room on the wooden floor. I tried to pray to stay in one spot, but there was a tremendous force that just kept on moving me in the circular pattern.

I met a new fried and invited him over to my house for dinner. After I gave him something to eat, I asked him if he drank red wine and said yes, so we went to the freezer and opened the freezer door and reached for a large bottle of red wine. Only a taste, I poured into the two clear glasses; the largest glass was mine. My friend said the wine was not too strong but was okay. After he drank the wine, his character changed; he started talking rapidly about all kinds of creative ideas. All of a sudden, he was standing by the wall elevated higher than me next to the bathroom. My sister-in-law came suddenly out the bathroom; I tried to introduce her to him but I had forgotten his name, so I asked him what did he say his name was. He said Dale. So then we went out on the town and saw some amazing architectural structures with buildings included. One was a huge pantheon spiral coliseum-type building made of multiple cylindrical columns. When you went up the steps, you could still see outside through the columns. Dale, my friend, had disappeared into the spiral maze of the building to my amazement.

I was in a classroom situation, and the teacher had given us a test on what we had read, but I didn't do so good and she told me so. There were many other students in the building, so I tried to get mad at the teacher for telling me this, I didn't understand the story in the book. So I left the classroom area and tried to understand why the teacher was so hard on me. It didn't make any sense. I thought maybe she was a racist, but whatever it was, I didn't feel good. I knew I had been gone for a long time so I knew when I got back to the lecture hall, she was going to ask me to where I have I been so long. So I thought I would tell her that I went to the bathroom. When I got back, a student was in the study area; he asked me what the story was about in his book. We were supposed to study and understand it. Of course, I looked at it and didn't really have a desire to read it or understand it. I told him he had to read it and understand it for himself. The teacher was in the lecture hall talking to a student when I came in. She asked me where have I been so long when I sat down by her, so I told her that I went to the bathroom. She said she didn't want to hear that shit. I told her that was not necessary, so now I really felt bad. Was I right about her? Then after a while, we had a break. Next, we were supposed to bring the teacher some work that we had researched and completed. She called me to her office. I sat down in a chair in front of her. She was also in a chair, and she started talking about my amazing strengths in her class, then she asked me a series of serious questions pertaining to an ancient planet and I remembered the information from a lecture she gave. I said that the planet was a geographical sphere in orbit in space, with very potent energy hits and is absorbed in half of the diameter of the planet at a ninety-degree angle, hits energy is activated every million years, and at that point, the planet's temperature was two hundred and ninety degrees below zero. I asked her did she live with the people there? She said yes, a long time before she became a teacher. Somehow, I knew the people were a dark color like the Eskimos. Right away, my feelings for the teacher changed. I realized who she really was. Trying to bring out the good strength in me, she was so into me. I wondered how she stayed warm and did she live with them below the surface of the planet. All these questions seemed to be answered in a flash in my mind.

I woke up in a bed in my room where there were some friends, relatives, and guests who were making merriment in my house; a festival or wedding was taking place. It seemed that they wanted me to join. But I wanted to take a run, so I did. I ran to a place where there were some vicious dogs, and they were locked up. After a while, the place was vacant and I was inside with no way out. Everything had changed, the dogs were gone, and everything was locked up.

I was outside in an area where there was a celebration going on. I had a little miniature flying electronic device; it was several sizes larger than both of my hands. There were people walking by waiting for me to activate it; the flying vehicle went into the air, circling around at various heights, then I made come it down with my own mind. Two people got into the vehicle and started again to go up and fly all through the clouds in the sky, then it came down again. This time, I got in; it flew so fast in the sky that I found myself hanging on with my hands on the back of the vehicle.

I was fighting a large short fat man; he seemed to want to destroy me in a place that was like a basement, but there was no out. I noticed that he had trapped or captured a young girl who was like in a hypnotic trance; she walked as if she didn't know who she was. We fought with iron bars. I escaped into the lower basement area where I saw there were great electronic machines with people locked down to them. There was still no way out. The people pulled the levers on the controls of the great electronic machines to blow up the buildings that they were trapped in.

I was looking at a newspaper with a picture of a heavy airplane in a cloud; a voice narrated the picture by saying even if the plane had strong winds hit it, the plane could still fly smoothly, then a voice called my name and woke me up.

A friend of mine wanted to cash a check; he couldn't decide whether he should go to the store or a friend of both of ours. I told him he should go to our friend who was at home. I had just talked to him. So he decided to go to the store, but then he asked me what I am drinking tonight. I told him I am drinking stout or light beer tonight; he looked at me a while. As I looked at him, I noticed that his head was somehow bigger; he said he would wait for me to freshen up.

I was given an award of a long golden sector rod and a medallion; two important woman gave a speech with the golden sector rod after it had been awarded to me. They did not give it back to me, and I was still waiting to receive my award back into my hands.

A pretty lady and I were going out together, but she got dressed before me. While I was dressing and putting my shoes on, she invited another man to come with us. She went with this man in a section of the closet and, looking at me at the same time, started to let the man make love to her with their clothes still on.

I was in a building with a young baby in my hands. I went into a large room where there were many children sitting up in their beds. But their bodies seemed to made out of a substance like plastic because they didn't look human; you couldn't see their irises, only their eye sockets. Their bodies were all in a vertical position, perfectly still like robots. As I walked closer to them, there was a bright light that shone into my eyes, so I stopped and went the other way.

I picked a DVD from the video rack in the store; the lady who I was taking to the show was wearing a yellow and white dress with a white hat, and I had just purchased a yellow bandanna to wear on my head. When I saw her, I had to go to the bathroom; after that, she gave me some packages of tea and asked me if I could make some tea for her before we go to the show.

I had won a prize, so I went to the place to collect my money. The man at the table said, "Here is your sixty-six thousand dollars." The money was all in a neat stack in paper money holders, so he told me to count it. Then a young lady came in and started to weigh items on a scale. Also, another man started to do some annoying activity, so I began to lose count. I actually tore the money, but then I realized I was counting a hard paper tag board. I saw the money still in a next pile on the desk. I told the man, "Why don't you just give me the money?" He said he couldn't do that because in Texas, they want certain consciousness. Then another man with a small tiny needle, which had a liquid inside of it, grabbed my hand even though I told him I don't need any more injections; he stuck the tiny needle into the side of the back of my hand. I felt a little drunk after that, then I told the man that told me about Texas that I am about universal consciousness. Before I could keep talking, a tall beautiful lady with her back turned to me appeared in front of me. I walked around toward her so I could see her face. She was very pretty. I said, "Don't I know you?" then she said yes. She put her arm around me and walked closely with me.

I was living in a nice neighborhood. I left my house to visit a friend. I saw a little girl crossing the street happily, and I said to her out loud, "Be careful so you won't get hit. "She was very happy and merry; when I saw my friend, we greeted each other and went inside his house. We talked for a while; he had a particular box on his living room table, and I asked him what was in it. He showed me that it could make fire. Then I told him I was going back home to do some painting and tai chi.

I went to a bakery to order something that had chocolate in it and saw that I had already some chocolate brownies in my garment pockets. So instead, I saw a long rectangular white cake and I asked the baker, "How much for that?"

And he said, "Seventy-five dollars for a special type of cake."

I said, "That much, huh, okay, I will take it."

Then he said, "Let me go and ask the boss," then a man came out who looked like a famous science fiction writer with a box to put the cake in. He gave me the box which had his name on it.

I had a little girl in my arms, trying to escape from animals in a city of broken and sunken streets. Cars were falling into deep cracks in the streets; one lady went into her car and spun into a crack and stopped at a halt, as she was at least several feet below the surface of the street. She seemed to be eating her dinner out of a bowl while she had been driving. I ran with the little girl away from the animals because our car had gone into a ditch in the street. I saw a house up on a green vegetated hill, so I went to it and went inside. I noticed that there was a bedroom and a place to stay for the little girl. But something wasn't feeling right, so I kept trying to get out of the house, but I kept coming to the same place, the bedroom, until finally, the last bedroom was larger, and there was someone in the bed that spoke words of entrapment. It seemed like a lady, but its voice was more like a man and robotic. The entity wore a mask on her face and held a mask in her hands. As she uncovered her face, she put a white turban on her head with a long white dress on. I noticed that I had touched sharp slender tubes that had blue and red liquid coming out of them. I thought maybe they were a drug to slow me down or poison me. Then with all my might, I tried to escape again, but she seemed to put her fingernails through my veins in my arm.

My friend played the flute where I had put two crystals in the front and the back so beautifully. He also played another instrument that was attached to it, a string drum, with grace. I played the string drum instrument together with a cousin of mine, but I had difficulty keeping up with the rhythm.

I met a beautiful young lady who I liked, and she liked me very much; she gave me the keys to her car. I waited for her at her office; she had gone to get some food. When she came back, she gave me a hug and said, "Let's go." But there was a lot of ice in her office, so I started gathering the ice up in a box from all over the floor. A man came in the office and started to question me as if I was playing with him. As I got ready to throw the ice out, the man ran out of the office, so I went out of the office and threw the ice on the street; the man stood far down the street, as if he were afraid of me throwing the ice on him. After that, me and my girlfriend left.

I was doing tai chi push hands with a master of tai chi; he defied the technique and began floating up into the air several feet. I went with him. But this made it difficult to uproot him because we weren't on the ground. When we finally came back to the ground, I did uproot him and take him to the ground with a head neutralization hold or press, but it was all in fun and love.

I created a 2-D net or weave pattern of an owl in the colors of blue thread. It was long in size and rectangular in shape. When I was working on it, I was very high on a monumental pole that overlooked the town and its people. When the townspeople came out of some buildings, they were in different groups. They all were talking among themselves of how I had created such a great work of art. They offered me accommodations; they seemed to know me. Then when I came down, I went to a new city with modern buildings and new people. I went to a place where my brother was and showed him the artwork. He though it was quite remarkable, so I let him keep it for a while and I ventured into the city. I went to a restaurant that was very exclusive. I met the same people who I had seen before in the other city; they were very happy to see me again. Again, they assured me that I could have this experience and anything else I wanted. Then I tried to get back to the place where my brother stayed, but the city looked entirely new and unique again. It was very hard to find the place again. Finally, I did run into my brother; he was saying something to me about the art, but I was trying to tell him that I had got lost, then he gave me the art back.

I was driven to a location in a car. I had a feeling the whole time that no one was driving the car, so when the car stopped and I got out, there was no one behind the steering wheel. I walked around the city, then I decided to take another cab. I knew I had enough money on my bank card for the ride. Somehow, the cab driver just appeared. He was a young man with tan skin and slim. He had a taxi van. I sat in the front seat with him; we almost hit a woman of color as she was crossing the street. She was not looking in the direction of traffic. I talked to her out of the van window and said that she should not be thinking about other things or daydreaming when she is crossing the street; she ignored me and turned her head away from me as we passed her by. Then we drove to an upscale part of the city to a new restaurant. I asked him what he thought about it. He said it's in the family, so it's good. But then I saw him adjust a handgun in his vest, the color was kind of bronze; he said you have to be protected.

As I sat in my friend's house, someone came in and walked by me with a long black veil-like cap on, mostly covering the body and face. I said to them, "Hey, man, what's happening?" But then, I sensed the gentleness and feminine aspect of the being, then I knew it was my friend's wife. So I said I was sorry.

"That's okay," she said. Her garment underneath the long black velvet cap was a grey shimmery color; she seemed to be looking for something. Then the husband came in, my friend, with the same type of clothes on that his wife had on. They both were looking everywhere for something. Then they went into their private chambers. I could still hear them communicating about something. Then they came out again without the hats on, but they were still looking for something. Some of their sons also came out looking for something. At one, I did hear him say that he was going to live the rest of his life with her. Then my friend said they were looking for some creature. I knew it was their pet lizard that had got loose in their house. I apologized and saw the biggest one. I quickly caught it with my hands, but it locked on to my hands with its teeth in its mouth. I could feel the sharp sticky teeth as I pulled its mouth off my hands. Then I hit its head several times to the ground to subdue it unconsciously.

I was running in a long-distance race, a marathon. I ran with other runners through various landscapes, buildings, and different neighborhoods, but I or any of the other runners did not know the race course; various people were telling us where to continue to run at various checkpoints inside and outside of various buildings. Sometimes, I had to wait a long time for someone to tell me where to run in the race.

I had a lot of money rolled up in a coil-like shape I put in my pocket. A woman of African descent, beautiful and dark with short hair, came to me humbly, begging for some money. She stopped me; it seemed as if she had some acute pain, and it was causing her to bend over. She said to me, "Can I ask you a question?"

I said yes.

She said, "Can you let me borrow three or four dollars please?"

So I said yes, but I told her that she would have to wait a minute. I would be right back. I was going to a bar where the bartender had refused to serve two drinks. That bartender said I took too long to tell him, when I was saying very loud, "Give me two ginger beers" because he seemed to be ignoring me; he got an attitude and gave me only one. So when I finally arrived to the bar, I couldn't find that bartender, so I went back to the beautiful African woman who stopped me, so I gave her the money that she asked me for, but she threw the dollars right into my face and eyes. So I asked her in shock but calmly why did she do that. So I counted the money again and saw that it was exactly six dollars and gave it to her. She took the six dollars and said that she was very sorry, as she walked by some people who were very rude to her. I followed her; she walked to an open place like a stage or open outside theater. She bent over in acute pain again. She was wearing a cut-out black t-shirt and a long black shirt, and as I looked closely at her stomach, I could see she was pregnant. She also had a little musical flute in the corner of her mouth. I mentally said to myself that I wanted that flute. Verbally, she told me the exact date and time that she would meet me again after she would have her baby. I agreed to the reunion and became very happy and was on my way running; when I looked back at her, she was still smiling and saying loving words to me. I ran through a beautiful African city; exotic beautiful young women dancers moved out of my way as I ran past them. The noble men and elders moved out of my way when I ran past them, but I didn't have any clothes on as I was running. I tried to cover myself with a little cloth, but I decided to keep on running naked. Finally, when I stopped running, I tried to play the flute that the beautiful African princess had given to me, but I couldn't get a sound out of it. It was a small narrow bone with skin over it; when I blew on it, the skin would inflate. I started to feel that this flute was an important connection for me and the African princess.

All the people in the church were vibrating with the Holy Spirit in several intervals of repetition; they seemed to shout at the same time, especially when the pastor said intensely, "So let it be."

The family man gave me a gift of a camera to take pictures. I was overwhelmed and I went to take pictures of a royal procession, but then, there was a special mechanical way to activate the camera. So I activated the camera, and I looked into the camera and saw a side long or distance shot of the participants in the royal procession, but I did not like this shot. So I went into a large brick building in front of the royal event. I was ready to film the royal occasion from closer frontal view and a male security guard tried to stop me. He ran magnetically after me, but for a time, I eluded him, then finally, he caught me and tried to lock me up in the building. He put a gun under my arm.

I sat there with the other athletes in the locker room; we gathered around the coach as he gave us a prep talk on winning, and all the time, he was looking at me as if I would surely win the race. I felt confident, strong, and powerful.

I ran into the house, and I felt as if I was trapped in the house. I went through the window and broke a glass small sculpture statue of the woman who owned the house. I ran through the neighborhood, seeing familiar faces and places, but I was trapped again in a different house and it had no doors. The windows were too small to get out.

My father had told me to stay at the top of a very high ladder. I didn't want to because it was so high up, but from there, I could see various cars with people traveling on the highways. One car was a fast red sports car with enough room for two people. The person driving the fast red sports car was driving at very wicked speed; the young man almost lost control of the sport car and went off the highway that was on a mountainside. Then I saw a young lady start to eat a wedding cake before the bride and groom had cut the cake. I tried to stop her by grabbing her and wrestling her to the ground, then I pinned her to the floor.

I visited a beautiful colorful woman; she invited me into her place. We talked and laughed for a long time. I looked closely into her eyes as I talked to her, then she asked me was I ready to leave and I said yes.

I was in a countryside home with beaches by myself. I was coming back from a run when a large group of people just came right into my home with love and friendship feelings. I didn't know them, but they wanted to share my food, books, and whatever I had with me. I told them I was so alone and I was happy to see them; they said that they were always here with me. I looked outside my place and saw that they had brought many boxes of things with them from large to small. I went outside and saw a beautiful young lady running toward me; it was raining only on her as she ran. Another young lady came up to me and said thank you and returned a book that she had borrowed.

The trumpet was five thousand dollars, and I had the money in notes but also in coins; the trumpet was gold, and the lady who wanted to sell me the trumpet took me to the back of the music store to meet her friends Also, there was a pair of running shoes for thirteen hundred dollars. I asked the salesman why they were so expensive. He said a great runner had ran in this style of running shoes.

There was a wild boar running fearfully back and forth, ramming its horn into a long and high wooden fence several times. The children had climbed high up in some tall slender trees above the wooden fence to avoid the boar attacks; at one point, it seemed to leap up as high as it could to hit the children with its long horn, but they were too high up. The boar kept getting its horn stuck in the wooden fence. Iran for a tree a little bit away from the side of the fence that the boar was on, I realized that the animal could come after me so I started to climb a tree, but before I could climb the tree, I saw all the children begin to turn cartwheel flips off the tree to the ground right in front of the boar, then continued to turn the cartwheel flips on the ground. The boar also began to turn cartwheel flips; there was a little boy in front of the boar walking backward, waving his hands up and down as if to hypnotize the boar. All the other children surrounded the boar and kept turning cartwheel flips, and so the boar continued to turn cartwheel flips also.

A famous movie star was thrown into jail; he went in. He was very muscular before he went in. My cousin and I were arguing about sexual energy; finally, I said it's different, but for me, all situations that I see with a man and a lady, whether I am involved or not, can enhance the sexual energy inside my body. My two sisters drove up to the jail to pick up the famous movie star. I saw my cousin leave me and go around the corner where we were talking in the parking lot outside of the jail to help escort the famous movie star to his car. As I stood up, I could see him give me a sign; he put his fist up in the air, so I did the same. I sat back down and wondered was I going to get a ride home because everyone was escorting the famous movie star. Next thing I realized that the famous movie star came around the corner and looked at me and said, "Come on, you know you're going to get a ride home."

Now I was so happy, I almost felt I wanted to cry but I didn't because the joy was so great. I got up and the famous movie star grabbed my hand. He looked like he had lost a lot of weight and muscle tone; also, he used a big word on me that I had never heard in the English content. We started to jog briskly to the car. I wondered if anyone was watching me hold hands with this famous movie star. As we jogged, I saw a hole in the ground and told him to watch out for it. He told me how he was subjected to certain chemical texts in jail.

THE LAST PART TO BLUEBERRY DREAMS

I WAS IN AN AIRPLANE and still on the ground; to my surprise, the window came automatically down a little next to where I was sitting on the plane, and I feel more air come in for me to breathe, but we never got off the ground or took off. We all got off the plane and walked into a terminal where there were many children and teachers outside. There, I noticed some of the children were hitting each other.

My family was throwing a surprise party for me, and when I got there, my oldest brother greeted me with a hug and handshake. We took off from the party early, and he was driving the car like a speed racer. I watched as he weaved and dodged through narrow spaces. Then he stopped the car and we got out and walked through a neighborhood that was cold like winter, cloudy with white clouds and white snow, and then we walked through a neighborhood with summer heat and blue sky and green vegetation. We entered into a house in one room where a young pretty woman greeted us. She looked very worried and asked her what was wrong and was she all right, then all of a sudden, she disappeared into a mirror wall in the room and she didn't come back. As my brother and I looked into the mirror wall, we could see faint figurative images dissolving softly out of focus, then my brother disappeared into the mirror wall. A strange bizarre feeling overtook me. I was in shock but happy. I ran quickly out the house shouting out loud the words, "Javu, javu, javu," into the neighborhood. I could see in the distance two-dimensional black Shallotte-like animals, hopping around the neighborhood houses.

There were millions of pyramids a mile high in the sky that covered the whole earth. They glowed with sunlight, a golden fluorescent color, and sent love and protection to the core of the earth. This love vibrated back out into the universe to all its stars and planets and beings. I could hear the whole universe singsongs of love.

The university was vast and extensive, build and carved out of solid rock. Everywhere I looked, it covered acres of green land. I felt like I wanted to go to this university; its color was burnt sienna, and all the windows were covered with stones.

I was talking to my mother; she was so beautiful and radiant, with her body so supreme. I felt so energized talking to her about the family. She wanted me to go to church for some special event. So I went. I was in a nice dark suit, and the church was very quiet and large. There were only a few men in the church. I helped the men open some very strange windows; they were very thick and dark, made of heavy glass and other solid materials. We had to turn small knobs clockwise to open the window just a half an inch or so. Earlier when I had come into the church, I had felt like these men were part of a secret group, but someone told me to be quiet so I did. Some of these men helped to open the windows in total silence.

I was a teacher in a classroom; there was a student who wouldn't be quiet and kept disturbing everyone in the class on purpose, so I asked him politely to be quiet several times, then an immense energy arose in me. I went back to him and picked him up with my two hands on the sides of his bald head and shouted to him to shut up, then I let him down and pounded my hand forcefully on his desk; the desk did not break, but then there was silence.

In the neighborhood, I was building a clay pyramid and rolling out clay in long coils. There were other people in the neighborhood working with clay also; at one point, I tried to make a clay wall by rolling it up with a sheet and putting clay with my hands over the exterior, but it didn't stay together. We had to clean up; we piled our clay tools into the neighborhood garage.

I was running in a city that had a lot of people on the sidewalks and streets, so I ran very carefully between them. I ran up a steep hill where children were playing. I saw two children that I had taught art in school. These two boys came after me and tried to tackle me, play-fighting in the process. I kept showing them handlock from the martial arts; every time they tried to wrestle me down, I would neutralize with hand and wrist locks. Then I ran around the city and their neighborhood again; finally, I went into one of the boys' home. I was standing hidden in one of the rooms listening to the boy tell his father the story of what happened with me. After he had finished, I came out of my hidden spot and kept looking at him so that he could finally notice me. Then he looked in my direction with surprise; before he could get to me, I ran off, out of the house and back into the neighborhood and the city.

I hadn't seen my friend for a long time; he looked very healthy and slim and trim. But I noticed that he didn't expect to see me. He was getting out of a car. I told him I could always come back to see him if he was too busy, then he kind of smiled and said that's all right. He introduced me to a friend of his, a mechanic, who had just finished working on a fantastic sports car; he shook my hand and proceeded right away to tell my friend the prize for the work which was one hundred and fifty dollars. My friend told me to come back in half an hour. He tried to wipe off some water on me with some napkins, then I noticed as I started to leave, his clothes changed into some sort of police uniform and went under some cars in the garage, moving like a snake and a worm.

I was running through a foreign city, trying to cross the street before cars drive past everyone else; there were so many strange buildings. One person was cleaning a building. I opened the door of the building; it was a dark bright green. It was an oriental building. There was another door to open. I looked up and saw it had oriental letters on it, so I didn't go in. I wanted to get to the library in the downtown area. So I kept running in the city along with everyone else, trying to cross the streets before the cars started to move. I noticed a woman's face close up; she looked like a German or Yugoslavian type. Her eyes were very large and she had a full face with big lips, light-brown skin, and green eyes. I ran past a hot chocolate drink vehicle, where I only saw men drinking chocolate and dogs inside the vehicle barking. As I ran by, it seemed that I was now far, far away from the library. I wanted to ask some people that I had passed along the way how to get there but I didn't. I looked out over the city horizon line and noticed that the city looked stranger than ever. There were buildings I had never seen before.

I was a student in a university class with other students; the women teacher called my name out to introduce me to the class. We took a break from the learning section. I went to an underground city where two huge men seemed to follow me for a while. Then I found the same class there with the same teacher. I wanted to live in two places.

I was running in slow motion from vertical highs and watching a person run behind me in a city of people and cars no matter how fast I wanted to run. I ran in slow motion, not in flat areas, but in high places from mountains to rivers to oceans waves rising and falling.

I had many teas and beautiful herbal products. I was placing these products in special boxes that had a dark-blue color made of a precious plastic leather to preserve them. I need a very tall ladder because I was placing the boxes on very high storage shelves outside about forty feet high or more. There was a lady and a man that I was talking to. The man got mad because my ideas were different from his. I told him he had a lot of pent-up disappointment in him, and that's why he was really mad with me. So he started to talk to the lady about how what I was saying made no sense, then I saw a slim light-brown-skinned man walking around underneath the place where I was placing the boxes with various herbal products; all of a sudden, he pushed the ladder in a way where it fell on some of the shelves and almost hit the lady and man who were talking. Some of the boxes came down too. The young man ran speedily to the edge of the building that we were on top of, and he jumped off about fifty feet to the ground and also ran swiftly after him and jumped off the building. I noticed as I was coming down, my body streaked like a rubber band, and I felt like I was descending in slow motion. When I hit the ground, I softly touched it with my two feet, and I felt no shock or weight of any kind. I saw that the young man had ran into a crowd of school children; he seemed a lot smaller now, a young boy with glasses. Before I could get to him, an adult male picked him up and sat him on his shoulders and started walking somewhere with him. As I looked at this, I decided to let him go.

I was walking up and down a busy street, passing many people on a sunny day. I saw a minister running very fast; he stopped and said to me that his running was a form of chi kung meditation, so I said to him if you take this standing pose and keep still with your palms facing to you, with your waist twisted a little and breathe slowly, you can increase your running ability. So he tried it; as he was doing it, a light-brown-skinned oriental well-built man came along and help me perfect the minister's chi kung. He said he was a chi kung master, then he went on to take off his shirt and show us some of his chi kung poses, which were excellent. He seemed to swell with more energy as he showed us the chi kung postures. When he was finished, he returned to his children and wife in the park. He seemed to be a very powerful man. I ran across the busy street, measuring my footsteps running and hopping together, because there were so many fast trucks and cars. But I got across easily and one lady followed me too. Then I saw a young woman in a parked car who seemed to have been resting there for a long time. She was very pretty and young, but she looked so calm.

I needed some help with my apartment; it was all covered in plastic and the bed and the floor were uneven. So the next time I went to my apartment, there were many man workers and big machines all around. In the building, everything had changed. I took out my key to open the door. There was a large metallic electronic box, so I pushed my key in it and turned it, a large copper-gold pole; it had the diameter of a large electrical pole. It came out of the top of the box and increased in size vertically as it went up about forty feet in the air until it reached the ceiling. Then a space in the ceiling of the warehouse opened up. The next moment I was inside of a large cavern carved out or dug out of solid rock. There were solid large oval-shaped windows that you could see clearly out of. We were very high up in elevation with a spectacular view. The floor of the cavern was highly polished and smooth; it was a silvery bright gray. A man who I didn't know was sitting next to me, telling me a story about the history of these caverns. Just like apartment complexes, there was more than one. He said that the caverns were carved out of solid gold. The room that we were in was so bright with so much sunlight that everything seemed to shine so brightly.

I was in a section watching a movie with other associates; when the movie was over, they asked me my opinion, and I said we should make our own movies. They asked me if I was ready, and I said yes. I had a camera that was triangular in my hands. The camera appeared out of nowhere. Then some gentleman came in and called my name and the other people in the room; he wanted our attention. The man started talking about some other event. He seemed to interrupt our discussion.

There was a party being thrown for a famous sandal maker in town; many people from various walks of life came to enjoy great cuisine and wine. I was running around, trying to help get everything in order, but I noticed that some of the people had already started eating; the famous sandal maker hadn't even arrived at the party yet. When she finally arrived, her cheeks were very rosy with a lovely smile; she was so happy to see the many guests.

I was eating some sweets with my sisters and looking at some pictures of my auntie. I began to communicate to her; she had become alive in the picture. So I asked one of my sisters if she could see the picture of my auntie and she said no. So I put the album book down and went into the kitchen because I knew there were more sweets, especially chocolate brownies there. I started to eat some of them, and then all of a sudden, my auntie appeared outside the kitchen door. The door was opened; she looked very robust and full of energy. Also, she was a bit heavier than what I knew of her when she was on the earth. I said to her as I went outside to greet her with a smile, "So you caught me in the act."

She smiled and told me to come with her for a ride. All at once, we were in a place that was like a huge garden, with trees and different plants. There was a small train that moved around in a circle. We got on it. I rode in an open cart behind her, and she rode in an open cart. We could see everything around us; my sister appeared and I told her, "This is the auntie that you couldn't see."

I went to the doctor's office to get medication for toothache; there were lots of people there. But a lady doctor motioned me to come forward. I saw a man who was in a state of paralysis; I asked him what had happened to him. He said he was getting too old and couldn't play the game of football like he used to. So I went into the lady doctor's office and she told me I didn't need medication, just come to her home and see her. That's all I need. I was surprised, so we left the office, then there was a woman coming by us who was carrying a baby which was crying; the woman wanted to talk to the doctor so I held the baby. The baby stopped crying; now the doctor wanted to take a picture with me, so the baby started to cry again. Someone took a picture of me in a sitting position holding the baby on a concrete slab with the lady doctor lying down behind, holding her head with elbow and hand. There was another child trying to get in the picture; the child climbed up on the concrete slab but couldn't make it up all the way. Then after the picture was taken, we all got into a cab.

I was in a place with teachers of levitation, so I asked the best teacher who levitated another person up in the air, "What is the secret to levitating up in the air?"

The teacher said, "You notice that I am hardly breathing."

I had prepared dinner for me and my girlfriend; we had just come back from walking in the park. We held hands, talked, and stepped slowly through the park. I wanted to eat right away the food which smelled and looked so good and warm. But my girlfriend was taking a bath and her sister went to the front door and opened it. Another boyfriend of my girlfriend was standing there; he said right away that he wanted to see me, so I came out to see him. He asked me did I take her to the park. I said yes, then he asked me if I had a car, and I said no, I don't have a car. He seemed like he was jealous, so I left him and went to take a bath. Then my girlfriend opened the bathroom door, and I said, "What?"

She said, "I just came to check on you."

I was in a place where the principal of our school led me into a large room where there were many puppy dogs of all breeds. I was trying to decide which one to adopt, some were gentle and some were fierce, but I never decided.

I was in a foreign land, Africa or another planet; the people there were all black, and I had been taken there by two relatives that had made the transition to another life. I remember going to a place, a large restaurant where a large bronze beautiful nude woman told me to come to her; she was at shrine doing some prayers. I watched her for a while, and she would melt down and move from one position to another, saying words softly, then she came to me and pulled me into the shrine area. She tied a white cloth around the top of my head, and then I stood in the middle of the shrine area; she stood at the entrance. As she turned her back to me, I looked and absorbed the beauty and strength of the fantastic black bronze woman, her legs, butt, and back monumentally strong and alluring. Then she began to dance rhythmically and gracefully in front of me in the entrance to the shrine. She asked for protection mainly and other blessings in an unknown language. Another lady came and gave her two long strong sticks, and she began to hit some type of gong by the shrine with them; this made a loud vibrating sound. I closed my eyes. When the sound had stopped, she came close to me and put both of her hands on my arms. I finally opened my eyes; she looked into them as I shook my head. I felt different; she smiled and said, "You will be okay."

I said to her, "Do you think it worked?"

She said yes and that we could do another one. She led me back into the restaurant where people were eating. I took off the cloth on my head.

I was in a classroom situation, trying to teach a group of students how to draw a truck, but every time I would try to say something to the students, a certain student would interrupt me. Finally, I started to knock out that student and all other students who kept interrupting me. Until there was a chilling silence, but I never did get to show them how to draw the truck.

I was at a university and a young man pushed a young woman to the floor. Then he pushed me. I didn't do anything because in my mind, I wanted to get the police, so I was calm. I finally saw the police and I told them what had happened. I asked them to give me their personal number in case this would happen again.

I knew that I had to be in school before eight o'clock; just because I live just a few blocks from school didn't mean I couldn't be late, so I tried to stay up all night as long as I could. Next thing I knew, I was waking up after falling asleep. I looked outside and I could see from my window that the children were going into the school, even though it was still dark outside, so I rushed to put on my pants and other clothes and wash my face. When I got into the school and entered the office to check in, I noticed that it was 7:46. I knew I was a couple of minutes late, so one of the secretaries said to me that I would miss nine days of pay for being so late. So I went to the principal who was also a lady and tried to explain that this was unfair. She told me to go back and try to talk to that secretary who had said that, so I did. I told her to look at my good standing performance here, I also said that her hairstyles were so unique and beautiful and that I always thought good of her. At that point, she kissed me on the lips and agreed with me totally.

We were in a place of electrical current. I had just won a Mercedes-Benz and was trying to get it charged for another person to drive it off to his place. Because I had lost my driver's license, so I found the correct cord with the current to charge it. So the man who was going to drive the Mercedes off to his house handed me some type of plastic thing that was one part dark black or brown and oval shaped. I didn't find the other part. He had been closely watching me before he gave it to me. I said to him, "So now you can drive the Mercedes-Benz to your home. I don't think I have to come."

He said, "You still have to come to practice your driving."

I realized that the cord was too short; how could I drive a long distance? Another man from the electrical shop said I can practice driving back and forth. At that point, I saw an image of a driver's license with my picture on it. It was in a violin case, so I picked up the violin case; it seemed very old. I opened it up slightly, when all of a sudden, a ray of strange light spiders sprayed out in a soft gust of air. I leaned back quickly, then a lot of ruby red bumblebees flew slowly out in slow motion until they weren't moving at all, but they were still in the air.

I was dodging them all the time, but one still landed on me.

I was in my bedroom looking out the window at night when I saw a giant grasshopper-like creature. I was very scared; after that, I was hiding in my bedroom closet hoping that creature would not come in through the window. I could see part of his head appear in the open window, so I knew he was going to come in. I looked for something to keep him from coming in, and I found a long narrow stick. I began to poke the creature with it from the window. I continued to poke him until he fell down and rolled and tumbled down a long narrow hill. At the bottom of the hill, his body seemed to lay still as if dead. I could see somehow the creature closely even though I was in my bedroom; he seemed to be more robotic than organic looking. Then I went out to help some children board a school bus. One of the parents had come on the bus to see if her child had boarded the bus; she had a very regal dark beautiful African face and so soft. I told her that I had killed a giant grasshopper. So I took her to the place where it had fell with the use of the lady's flashlight; the creature was not there anymore.

We were all in room talking many people, and then I saw a man who I knew as a great martial artist; he had pass away from this earth. He was dressed in a golden green outfit. He told me I was in a good place. I asked him were there many ladies where he was at; also, I asked him how life was now. He told me it was very slow, like slow motion I was running so fast that I outran a red car on the road; the driver of the car pulled in front of me several yards and stopped the car. When the person got out from the passenger side, it was a large grizzly bear, coming quickly toward me, growling at me. I tried to run rapidly away from it and find some steel covering like a garbage can top to protect myself.

I was with a lady; we were both plainclothes police. We were in a church meeting with various people, talking and shaking hands. We had our guns on us, but my partner was telling me that I should put my gun into my pocket, but you could still see it then. We got on the bus and didn't have to pay.

I had gone to an art gallery that was being remodeled. I could see that there was a working format or large cloth put over the whole gallery. All the doors and windows were closed, but I knew the men had to be working on the gallery somewhere. I took off my shoes and started looking around for the cruise. I ran around the art gallery on the outside. I could feel my feet on the ground; also I could remember being taken on a tour of the gallery before by one of the men who worked at the gallery. Finally, I looked over the top of the gallery and could see the man on the roof, the inner part; they were working and painting the art gallery. So I started to run back to the front of the gallery where I had taken off my shoes. As I ran, I could feel some magical atmosphere and the knowing that I had ran this same path before in another time. When I saw my shoes, they were very small, and they were being put on by some little human character. I asked him, "Would he give me back my shoes and make them bigger again?"

The little human character did make them bigger and gave them back to me. I tried them on and they fit perfectly, but they still look different, softer, and lighter. Also there was another little human character who was trying on shoes there too.

I was at a symphonic concert, sitting in seats in a large auditorium; the orchestra was playing brilliantly, but someone had closed the doors in front of the orchestra. Even though these doors were not big, they seemed to close off the huge orchestra. The sound of the music was hardly noticeable. Now appeared a giant metallic sound speaker that looked like a robotic face in front of us. The audience could now hear the sound of the orchestra clearly through this speaker, but a man and a woman went up and moved some parts on the robotic face and there was no more sound. My friend went up and moved some parts of the robotic face and the sound came back again, but the same man and woman went up and moved some parts on the robotic face again to turn the sound off. My friend left, so I went out to see an old part of the city that I had only seen a long time ago. It was an island but very high up on a mountain. When I got there, the lights were very bright and the houses were built on a series of hills. There were no stairs to get to the houses or leave the houses, so I just slid down the highly polished granite walls of the mountain, and to get to the houses, I walked up the grass. I walked around and looked at some of the houses. I met a fellow walking up the grass in the area. He greeted me with a smile and put his arm to my arm adjacent, side by side, in a friendly gesture. Also he said a special greeting to me that made me feel good. Inside the island, there was a lower level that was very dark with just small amount of dim light. But I felt like I could see from a high-level distance another land mass farther away from the island. I knew that this was the first time I had explored the island. I was ready to get back home so I went to the bus station. I showed the officer my ID, and he told me that I was only supposed to get paid once, but it looked like I got paid three times. I told him no, it's a mistake.

I was sleeping in a queen-sized bed with the cover over me, a thick warm cover. I felt like I was falling while I was sleeping; the feeling woke me up, then I started to see energy pattern glisten in the invisible air. In the bedroom, I chased after these patterns, and when I intersected these patterns with a moving stick or shirt, they would immediately turn into butterflies, like white silvery shapes, and disappear. Then I put my clothes on and took a walk in the hills not too far from where I lived in a small bungalow apartment complex. I looked back, and I could see a strange man dressed in very conservative clothes, asking questions to the tenants in the place where I lived. I quickly rushed back to my house, and when I entered, I saw a large brown-skinned man and many prepared dishes of sweets set out so nicely in my place. They were made up of so many bright colors and also a lot of chocolate chip cookies too. The large brown man said he wasn't ready for me yet, but he would leave now, but there were several children at that moment who just came into my house; they were his children. Some were young boys; some were young girls. The brown man started to ask me a series of questions about an old-fashioned record player that was made of wood in a large rectangular shape; one of his young daughters tried to sit on it. I told her she would break the needle if she sat on it. But she kept trying to sit on it several times. I finally had to gently lift her up and put her back down away from the record player. Then I sat on the large rectangular wooden record player to protect the turntable and needle. A different child now sat next to me and put out their arms around me, then another child gave me an empty small milk carton, that had print awards for some game written on it. I read the details; one of the prizes was an expensive car. After that, all the children gave me a huge hug and left. They were very happy.

I was in line in a medium-sized store that made various homemade juices. It seemed that the line of people kept getting longer and longer, even though no one was getting in front of me. I felt like I didn't have a particular place in the line. The amazing thing is that they had different-sized porcelain containers that they sold the juices in, five gallons to fifty gallons. For the customers to see the juices before the container was filled, the people at the counter would tilt the container so that some of the juice would spill on the floor; after seeing that and noticing all the many people in line, I left the store. I walked down the street of a bright sunlit city; all of a sudden, there were gunshots. I could hear some people from a nearby church say that he was playing dead, even though he was the one that fired the shots. As I kept walking, I came to a tall building and went inside; there was no one there. I came to a door and opened it, and I realized I was inside a vast computer. I was at the top looking down on my side going down to three hundred feet about; there were many electronic configurations that had window-like screens. At the bottom on the other side facing me, there were many metallic doors that looked like elevator doors that had many dates of the year at the top of them, 1911 or 1414. Also on the other side of the bottom where there were no elevators, there was coral from the sea and beautiful mermaid-like female creatures transformed from the coral and gliding effortlessly to the window parts and screens to put in data. Then when they finished, they would go back into the coral; there were about fifty mermaids all together. The sight of this made me feel uneasy because I knew I was seeing something from another world. The beautiful mermaid female creatures didn't even notice me. I wanted to leave this place, but there was no way out. As I looked around, I saw how humans were getting onto the elevators as the doors opened up. So I went down to the elevators, I noticed that they all had different dates on their doors. There was a lady getting on an elevator that said 1914, so I felt that was the one to get on. But as the door closed, I said to myself, "I don't think this is the right one because the date changed to 1114, but we seemed to be standing still."

I was sitting in my house when a family came to visit me; the children were very happy. The father had an object that was three-dimensional and oval shaped and had a golden coin for the bottom and a dome made of a clear material that you could see through, like glass. There was nothing inside; you could only see the golden coin at the bottom. The coin was about an inch in diameter. The father put the object on the table and pressed down on the top of it gently. The whole object disappeared for a long time, then it reappeared in its original place. I was trying to explain the theory behind this happening, but the children kept interrupting me. So this time, I pressed on the top of the object with my finger, and it disappeared again for a long time; this time it came back to the lap of the father. He put it back on the table, but his little daughter tried to take it apart, but I grabbed her by her arms and put her on the floor. The father mentioned to me that she would not destroy the object, then I watch her change into a little bird walking around on the floor. Then some mice came after her. I started to tell the parents about a funny time when some rats came into my house, but I didn't finish the story. I looked back at the little bird; the little bird was knocking the rats out by using kung fu kicks and pecking them. I wondered to myself, *Why doesn't the little bird just fly away?* Now the rats changed into little wooden men that were drunk after the little bird had attacked them.

It was the New Year's Eve, and we, my friends and I, were at my oldest brother's house. I wanted to go home to change into party clothes, but my oldest brother said I could change at his home into some of his new party clothes. I saw that he had several new colorful pair of pants. I tried one pair, the color which was navy blue, so I started to walk around in the pants, and when I looked down at them, they had changed to half yellow and half gold. I told my oldest brother that the pants changed color by themselves. Then I tried a short sleeved shirt on. I noticed that all the men were wearing the same shirt, and we all looked great. We all wanted to go to the strip club, but for some reason, my oldest brother said he was getting married tomorrow, so he didn't want to go. So some of the man went to a party down the street. One of the man stayed with me, but he had spilled some orange type of drink all over his shirt. The other men went with my oldest brother to a conservative house party. The man with the spoiled shirt and I started to walk and it began to rain; we went to a covered bus stop area by the street. The man with the spoiled shirt was sitting and I was standing. I asked him if he was going to his house to change his shirt, and he said yes. But then I noticed that the man now changed into a lady.

I was on a school bus with a group of very young students from school; the children started to make noises on the bus and started talking to me, saying a lot of things that didn't make sense. So I was there sitting with my sister, ignoring them completely. Finally, our stop came and we got off the bus so did the children. My sister went home and I continued walking in another direction; the children followed me and continued to talk to me with harassment. Then a man came by and asked me what was happening. I told him that these children won't go home and continued to follow me, talking nonsense. Then in another direction, there was a man with some type of strange animal fighting another strange type of animal. The man that asked me what was happening stopped the other man from fighting his strange animal with the other strange animal. One of the strange animals was damaged, so we went close with caution to look at his damaged foot. But we also noticed it had several feet and black fur; we couldn't see its head. After all, this had happened the children were all gone.

After a carnival celebration, I looked out of my upstairs bedroom window and saw some children trying to come up a ladder to my house. I told them I would push the ladder down if they continued. So I did push the ladder down, then I went downstairs to see what happened; now they were inside my house.

Two of them held up some guns. I shouted out to them, "Go ahead and shoot."

There was silence for a while, then they didn't shoot, so I told them that I would get the police on them, then they left.

I was talking to a beautiful lady on a balcony overlooking the ocean several hundred feet up; all of a sudden, a large black falcon glided in front of us over the rail of the balcony down to surface of the ocean. Then the beautiful lady suddenly jumped over the rail of the balcony all the way down to the ocean's surface, so I too jumped over the balcony rail; my whole body on the way down felt like a rubber band, but I made it to the surface of the ocean in seconds I was playing my flute in a large mall; there were many people dancing and moving around to the sound of my flute. I was on top of a window ledge, so I had to be careful because I didn't have a lot of space to move around in and play. At a certain point, my flute turned into a trumpet and then I really started to play wonderfully. People were smiling at me and saying hello, especially ladies. Some man who was young and light skinned came by me and gave me a tap on the ankle. Then I stopped playing and climbed slowly down through the window that I had been playing my trumpet in front of to the other side opposite the mall. On the other side, there were many people moving from place to place. I turned around and closed the window. The man who had tapped me on the ankle got up onto the window ledge where I had been playing the flute and trumpet and started talking to the people in the mall about some type of promotion. Then he came to the window and put his face close to it as if he was looking at something beside me. His head turned into a head of a manikin or dummy, then I actually turned his head around without opening the window to the people in the mall that he had been talking to. After that, his body came back to his head, and he became alive again to the people in the mall. There was also a beautiful young lady who got up on the window ledge with him and talk to the people about the promotion as well.

I was running a race through a city with a well-known superstar woman. I was right up there with her running, then all of a sudden, I was in a truck with a driver that I knew from way back; somehow without me knowing it, he had picked me up from the race and another runner as well. I told him that he should have never picked me up because he wanted to continue to run against the running superstar lady. So he finally dropped me off on the race course. I tried to catch up with the running superstar lady, but another runner on the course tried to block my way by running in front of me to slow me down. I told him that he couldn't block me, but then he held my hand to prevent me from running at all. So I hit him and he fell down and turned into some kind of animal. So I started to run again until I lost my way in the route; some people on the race course told me to go down some stairs into a tunnel because that where the superstar lady runner went running, so I went running down into the tunnel and everything vanished.

I was with a friend high up on top of a mountain, looking at a tidal wave engulf a seaside village. After it was over, my friend and I explored the village; we found that there were many ruins there, and one of them was a coral reef ancient city. The city had many tunnels that were large enough to walk through easily.

There was a driver driving me and some school children from school; one child jumped off the vehicle while we were moving and she would fly back on. She had magical powers that I knew of. She did it again, and I told her to hurry up and get back on. She floated horizontally in the air about twenty feet away from the vehicle, then she glided in the air back onto the vehicle. Some of the other children who had got off too, who didn't get back on, were left behind; the girl decided to go back and be with them. She flew rapidly in the air back to them. As we, the driver and I, kept going with the other children, I could see in a distance that there were several volcanoes in the city that were boiling up with white lava. The white lava eventually came out, spilling over into the streets and houses of the city. So we drove to higher ground. Then the atmosphere became very cool and dark, then it started snowing lightly. We were now in a very calm, peaceful part of the city. I saw a tall slim dark lady in a pantsuit with a round hat on, walking up the street; she waved gently at me. As I said hi, I realized that I had known this tall young lady before.

My friend and I talked about how great are mothers are even though they had left the earth. He said my mother was so sweet and I told him his mother was also so sweet; he just wished he could have done more for her while she was on the earth. I told him that he still can.

As I stood there next to the old-time piano, the longtime old friend, a beautiful lady teacher, and an excellent cook sang a song to me about how God is preparing for a lovely wife and that I will not get everything when I want it but only when God has prepared me for it. I humbly listen to the inspiring lyrics that she sang soulfully.

There were many people in a sleeping bunker that had many beds for everyone. I slept in several of the beds, but I noticed that I never went to sleep, In the morning, we all went to brush our teeth and wash up in several bathrooms. It seemed as though I was watching everything from a distance. There was one young man that who flooded the upper bathroom with water; everyone was annoyed with him.

I went to see a famous musician practice with his band a new song. Everyone looked so serious; a famous singer who I knew came in and sat in a chair next to me, but she did not notice me for a long time. She was enjoying the music, then after a long time, she finally said hi. One of the musicians, the trumpet player, was looking for his horn, and when he found it, the trumpet was stuck to the table, so he just played on his mouthpiece. Then the famous musician I noticed was looking at me, then when he knew that I knew he was looking at me, he stopped looking at me.

Printed in the USA
CPSIA information can be obtained
at www.ICGtesting.com
LVHW082118061023
760262LV00008B/1093